Contents

PREFACE TO THE 14TH EDITION

SINCE the first edition of *How to Cover the Gaps in Medicare* was published over twenty years ago, a virtual revolution has occurred in the Nation's system of health care for senior citizens. The costs of health care, Medicare, and health insurance are much more than they were then. At the same time, remarkable advances in health care have allowed more people, including those with chronic health problems, to live longer and better lives than ever before. Prescription drugs played such a minor role in the treatment and prevention of illness when Medicare was created in 1965 that they were not covered by the program. Now they have moved to the forefront of medicine.

The care needs of seniors who can no longer live independently were once filled mainly by nursing homes, but alternatives have proliferated in the past decade. These include continuing care retirement communities, assisted living facilities, and home care services. As the American population ages, the range of options that are available to seniors for both living arrangements and long-term care will continue to evolve.

It would be impossible in a general discussion to describe in great detail all of the ramifications of current health care and long-term care trends, or all of the opportunities available to people in different circumstances. It is possible, however, to describe the principal considerations that all of us ought to take into account when we plan for our own futures – and when we exercise our rights as citizens in choosing what type of health care system will provide widest accessibility to the best medical care at the lowest cost.

Part 1 of this book briefly describes the history and current provisions of Medicare, which has undergone numerous changes in recent years. It also traces the history of the "medigap"—the portion of senior health care costs that is not covered by either Medicare Part A or Part B. This gap poses a significant financial risk to Medicare enrollees.

Part 1 also discusses the Medicare Prescription Drug, Improvement, and Modernization Act of 2003. Signed by President Bush in December 2003, this law authorizes the most significant expansion of Medicare since the program was created. It increases government

1

funding for Medicare HMOs and adds new benefits for Medicare enrollees. Most important, it creates a new Medicare prescription drug benefit. Beginning in 2006, seniors will have the opportunity to buy Medicare-backed prescription drug insurance. Chapter III describes this benefit and other provisions of the new law.

Part 2 describes Medicare Advantage – the new name for Medicare + Choice, the Medicare program that allows private companies to offer you your Medicare benefits. This program allows you to choose, subject to availability, among a variety of plans, such as managed-care plans (HMOs), private fee-for-service plans, and preferred provider organizations (PPOs). Part 2 also describes the Medicare supplemental insurance that is available to Medicare enrollees who choose to remain in the original Medicare program. Chapters VII, VIII, and IX review the ten standardized "medigap" policies and provide criteria for selecting one.

Part 3 discusses long-term care options. Many individuals are understandably concerned that the costs of long-term care in a nursing home will leave either themselves or their spouses financially destitute. In fact, there are a variety of protections against the costs of such care. These include long-term care insurance, continuing-care retirement communities, assisted living and home-care alternatives. Many "middle class" seniors may also find that with careful planning they can become eligible for Medicaid. However, the rules and penalties relating to transfers of assets in order to become eligible are tighter than they once were, and fiscally-burdened states are seeking even tighter restrictions.

Part 4 considers end-of-life decisions that have been necessitated by court rulings relating to "right-to-die" issues. The fact is that your wishes regarding the type of medical care that you receive if you become unable to make your own decisions probably will not be honored unless you follow the specific procedures mandated by "living will" statutes. Separate "health care proxy" laws allow you to appoint someone you trust to make health care decisions for you. Even the most carefully prepared documents cannot guarantee that your wishes will be carried out. However, if you have not prepared a living will and a health care proxy, it is almost guaranteed that they will *not* be.

Appendix A considers some of the issues that have framed the debate over public versus private health care systems, and which promise to attract greater public interest as the costs as well as the benefits of public health care become more apparent.

Lastly, Appendix B provides a list of useful publications that you can get from Medicare. Too few seniors are aware of the information and assistance that is available from Medicare, free for the asking. The phone numbers and websites of many other helpful agencies and organizations, public and private, are mentioned throughout the book.

The task of insuring oneself against the risk of illness in old age is growing increasingly complex. At the same time, the risks of *not* insuring oneself are more threatening than ever. It is our hope that the pages that follow will be useful as an introductory guide to obtaining whatever protection is available.

Part 1
THE MEDICARE QUANDARY

I.

THE HEALTH INSURANCE PRINCIPLE

A S with other forms of insurance, the purpose of health insurance is to reduce the financial burden of risk by dividing losses among many individuals. In general, health insurance in America has worked much as life insurance, homeowners' insurance, or automobile insurance. The insured pays the insurance company a specified premium and the company guarantees some degree of protection. And like other types of insurance, health insurance premiums and benefits are figured on the basis of average experience. In order to fix rates and benefits, insurance company actuaries rely on aggregate statistics that tell them how many people in a certain population group will become ill and how much their illnesses will cost.

Here the similarity ends. Unlike life insurance or homeowners' insurance, the value of health insurance is *not* measured by the actual amount promised as a benefit—as in a $25,000, $50,000, or $100,000 life or homeowners' policy. And unlike automobile liability insurance, which fixes a limit on the amount that the company will pay, health insurance is "open-ended." That is, no one can say what the maximum benefit return on any given policy will be. Health insurance limitations often are measured *by time* (90 days, 6 months, 1 year, etc.) rather than by dollar amounts. Unlike other forms of insurance, the value of health insurance is measured according to the extent to which it reduces *potential risk* in the event of illness. That is, *how much would the patient still owe after all insurance benefits were exhausted?*

The Unpredictability of Illness or Infirmity

From the individual consumer's perspective, illness or infirmity must be regarded as totally unpredictable. No one can predict when illness will strike or what form it will take. Nearly everyone has friends or loved ones who have been hit out of the blue with serious illness or disability. And often the reaction is: "I never would have believed it could happen to him." Conversely, we all know people who for years think they are desperately ill, yet live on to a ripe old age. In short, sickness—as well as good health—often comes as a surprise. The belief that we can easily predict the future seems to be

7

a persistent type of human behavior (especially among some economists who ought to know better). It must, however, be excluded from any thought regarding health insurance.

It is also crucial that *average risks* not be confused with *potential risks*. Insurance companies structure policy coverage and premium rates around the likelihood of certain conditions occurring. To be sure, a certain percentage of a specified group of people will contract a certain disease or become disabled. But this average risk experience is of little practical value to the individual.

Instead, the insurance buyer must be concerned with potential risks that seldom occur, but that everyone nevertheless faces. This point is of the utmost importance, since many insurance companies cite *average statistics* in their sales promotions. Far too many people have been misled by sales presentations giving general figures that frighten them into believing they will contract a certain disease or require a certain type of care. Some companies have relied almost exclusively on the power of such frightening figures to generate purchases of their policies. Again, although the averages may be accurate, they bear no relation to the potential risks arising from the unpredictability of illness.

A hypothetical case from a less emotionally charged situation will illustrate the point. Let us assume for the sake of example that more automobiles are painted white than any other color and that *on average* white cars are involved in more accidents than any other. The question is, would you purchase automobile insurance that protected you only in the event that a *white* automobile collided with you? Obviously not.

The unpredictability of illness and health care costs during recent decades has thrown the health insurance industry into disarray, and this fact has important implications for all health insurance buyers—elderly or not. Aside from the unpredictability of illness, the costs of diagnosing and treating many conditions are uncertain. First, medical technology is rapidly altering diagnostic and therapeutic procedures for most illnesses. Sometimes the actual costs go up, and sometimes they go down. Second, illness varies from place to place and from population to population. There is no reliable way of predicting what will happen in any given area on the basis of aggregate experience. Third, and most important, health care costs vary greatly.

Historically, hospital and doctor fees have varied widely from place to place. Medicare administrators have attempted to regulate both hospital and physician fees. But these attempts have introduced new factors that have further complicated Medicare reimbursement procedures.

The consequences of these uncertainties—all of which are related to the unpredictability of illness—are enormous. To a greater extent than in other types of insurance, actuarial "science" in the health insurance field is unreliable.

The result has been an enormous variation in premiums and losses, and this has offered tremendous variation in value for the health insurance buyer. The periodic changes in Medicare itself also affect what you should look for in supplemental insurance policies and other alternatives that protect you against the "medigap" (what you owe after Medicare has paid its portion of your medical bills). In short, it may pay to expend considerable effort in understanding Medicare, "medigap" insurance, and long-term care insurance before making any major decision regarding your health care coverage in retirement. Unfortunately, an uninformed decision now could prove costly at a later date. We hope that this book will be a useful resource to help you make informed choices.

II.

MEDICARE

MEDICARE is the Federal health insurance program that covers virtually every one of the more than 35 million Americans age 65 or older, as well as more than five million Americans with permanent disabilities who are under the age of 65. The Medicare program, enacted on July 30, 1965 as Title XVIII of the Social Security Act, became effective July 1, 1966. It consists of two separate parts, Hospital Insurance (Part A) and Supplemental Medical Insurance (Part B).

Medicare coverage initially included only Social Security retirement beneficiaries but subsequently has undergone many changes. Over time the Medicare program has been extended to provide coverage to disabled persons entitled to monthly cash benefits under Social Security or the Railroad Retirement program; to pay benefits for hospice care for terminally ill patients; to make Medicare the secondary payer for all workers aged 65 or older and their spouses who are covered by employment-based health insurance; to include payment for immunosuppressive drugs to transplant patients; to provide home health care benefits; and to provide coverage for mental health services. Most recently, in December 2003 President Bush signed the Medicare Prescription Drug, Improvement, and Modernization Act. This legislation marks the biggest expansion of Medicare since the program was created.

Who is Eligible for Medicare?

Anyone 65 or older who is entitled to monthly benefits under the Social Security or Railroad Retirement program—or would be entitled if an application had been filed—is automatically eligible for premium-free benefits under Medicare's **Hospital Insurance (Part**

FOR MEDICARE INFORMATION

Call 24 hours a day, including weekends

1-800-MEDICARE (1-800-633-4227)

TTY 1-877-486-2048

Visit www.medicare.gov

A). Persons who are already receiving Social Security benefits will be automatically enrolled in Medicare Part A when they turn 65. Otherwise, you must enroll in Medicare by calling the Social Security Administration at 1-800-772-1213. You may also apply online at www.ssa.gov. You can receive Medicare benefits even if you continue to work. Currently, the age of eligibility for Medicare is still 65, even though the full retirement age for Social Security benefits is now higher than that and is scheduled to gradually rise to 67 for those born after 1937.

In addition, several other classes of persons, who must apply for coverage, are eligible for Medicare Part A, including:

- any disabled individual under age 65 entitled to monthly disability benefits for a total of 24 months (not necessarily consecutive) under Social Security or the Railroad Retirement program (spouses and children of disabled beneficiaries are *not* eligible for Medicare benefits); disabled persons who become ineligible for Social Security benefits because their earnings exceed the maximum allowed have the option to purchase Medicare coverage;

- anyone under age 65 who has end-stage renal disease and who meets certain work requirements for "insured" status under the Social Security or Railroad Retirement programs, or is entitled to monthly benefits under these programs or is the spouse or dependent child of such an insured person or beneficiary. Eligibility begins on the first day of the third month following the month in which either dialysis terminates or the individual has a renal transplant;

- anyone under age 65 who has Lou Gehrig's Disease (ALS). Coverage begins the first month you get disability benefits from Social Security;

- anyone aged 65 or older enrolled in the Medicare Supplemental Medical Insurance program (Part B) who is not otherwise entitled to Part A benefits, upon voluntary participation with payment of a Part A premium. (The full Part A premium in 2004 is $343 per month.) Persons who do not purchase Part A coverage within a specific time after becoming eligible because of age are subject to a 10 percent penalty for each 12 months they are late in enrolling. However, the 10 percent penalty will be charged against the Part A premium for only a specified time period (twice the number of years enrollment was delayed), after which the penalty will be eliminated and the premium levied as though no delay in enrollment had occurred.

Medicare **Supplemental Medical Insurance (Part B)** is available to anyone age 65 or older who is a U.S. citizen or a lawfully admitted alien with five years continuous residence. More generally, it is available to anyone of any age who is entitled to Medicare Part A benefits. If you are receiving Social Security or Railroad Retirement benefits, you will be automatically covered by Part B insurance when you enroll in Part A, unless you tell Social Security that you do not want Part B. The premium for Part B ($66.60 per month in 2004) is deducted from your monthly Social Security or Railroad Retirement benefit. If you do not receive such benefits, Medicare sends you a bill for your premium every three months.

If you have turned 65 and want to delay your Social Security benefits, your enrollment in Medicare Part B is not automatic; you have to apply for it. If you do not enroll in Part B during your initial enrollment period but later decide you want benefits, you can sign up during the general enrollment period each year (January 1 through March 31). However, your benefits will not begin until July 1, and your monthly premium will rise by 10 percent for each 12-month period you are not enrolled in the program. The period subject to this late enrollment penalty does *not* include months during which you (or your spouse) were working and covered by employer-sponsored health insurance.

If You Retire Before You or Your Spouse Has Reached Age 65

For most persons, Medicare eligibility begins at age 65. If you retire before that time, you should, if possible, make arrangements to continue the employer-sponsored health plan that provided coverage while you were working—or to convert that insurance to an individual policy, an option that in most instances is required by law (within specified time limits).

If you retire at age 65 and become eligible for Medicare but your spouse is under age 65, current law in most states requires that group insurance carriers permit the coverage of a spouse and other dependents to be continued under the employer-sponsored plan. However, the employer has no responsibility to contribute toward the costs of such insurance and the retiree will have to pay whatever premiums are required to keep it in force.

Medicare Part A

Under the Medicare benefits structure now in effect, Medicare Hospital Insurance (Part A) pays most hospital costs for the first 60 days of hospitalization after a deductible amount of $876. After that, Medicare pays the balance of covered costs after the patient pays $219 per day for the next 30 days and $438 per day for the following 60 "lifetime aggregate reserve" days. After 150 days of continuous hospitalization, Medicare Part A pays no benefits. Once the 60-day lifetime reserve has been used, it cannot be applied to subsequent illnesses. Should a new episode require hospitalization after the lifetime reserve has been expended, Medicare Part A benefits will cease after 90 days of confinement.

Medicare Part A also pays for the costs of 20 days in a skilled nursing facility after a hospitalization of at least three days and all but $109.50 per day of skilled nursing home costs for the next 80 days. After 100 days of such confinement, Medicare Part A pays nothing.

Medicare Part A helps pay for home health care and hospice care. Home health care includes part-time skilled nursing care, physical therapy, and durable medical equipment (such as wheelchairs, hospital beds, oxygen, and walkers). Hospital Insurance covers the first 100 visits following a hospital stay of at least three consecutive days or a skilled-nursing facility stay. You must pay 20 percent of the approved amount for durable medical equipment.

Hospice care includes medical and support services from a Medicare-approved hospice, drugs for symptom control and pain relief, and care in a hospice facility, hospital, or nursing home when necessary. Home care is also covered. You pay $5 for outpatient prescription drugs and $5 per day for inpatient respite care (*i.e.*, short-term care given to a hospice patient by another care giver so that the primary care giver can rest). To receive hospice care, patients must be certified as being terminally ill. Benefit periods include two 90-day periods, followed by an unlimited number of 60-day periods.

The table on page 16 provides a more detailed summary of current Medicare Part A benefits and the beneficiary's financial risk for uncovered services.

Medicare Part B

Medicare Supplemental Medical Insurance (Part B) is offered to eligible Medicare beneficiaries on a voluntary basis. The premium is $66.60 per month in 2004. Part B pays 80 percent of Medicare's "approved charges" for covered services after you pay a deductible of $100 per year. Covered services include doctor fees, outpatient hospital care, and durable medical equipment.

The table on page 17 provides a more detailed summary of current Medicare Part B benefits. The boxes on pages 20 and 21 list specific items that are and are not covered under Medicare Part B. However, keep in mind that this list is subject to change, especially as the provisions of the Medicare Act of 2003 are phased in. If a particular test, service, or item was not covered in the past, you should check with your doctor or with Medicare to see if it is now. For example, Medicare coverage for preventive measures (such as mammograms and colorectal cancer screenings) has expanded over the years, and the 2003 legislation added more preventive benefits. These include blood tests for early detection of heart disease, diabetes screening tests for high-risk people, and, beginning in 2005, a one-time "wellness" physical exam within six months of the day you enroll in Medicare Part B.

Medicare Part C

Medicare Part C was enacted in 1997. Originally known as Medicare + Choice, its name was changed by the Medicare Act of 2003 to "Medicare Advantage." Part C expanded some non-traditional health care options, such as HMOs, that were already available to Medicare enrollees. It also created incentives for the introduction of other private market-based Medicare health plan options for beneficiaries. The goal was to provide an alternative to participating in the traditional Medicare plan and purchasing a supplemental insurance (medigap) policy.

Medicare Advantage health plans, such as HMOs, cover everything that traditional Medicare covers. Most plans also cover additional services and items. Some plans charge an extra premium be-

MEDICARE BENEFITS SUMMARIZED AND PATIENT FINANCIAL RISK
HOSPITAL INSURANCE — PART A

Type of Service	Time Limit	Patient Risk	Medicare Pays	Qualifications	Exclusions
Hospital Confinement: semiprivate room and board unless a private room is required for medical reasons. Covers routine nursing, drugs, and normal services, including operating and recovery rooms, medical social services, physical therapy, equipment and medical supplies.	First 60 days each benefit period*	**First $876**	Balance	Age 65 and: (1) Entitled to Social Security (or Railroad Retirement) benefits; or (2) is *not* entitled, a citizen or permanent resident for 5 years, may enroll by paying a monthly fee plus Part B (cost below).	First three pints of blood, private duty nurses, noncovered levels of care, services covered under Part B, television, telephone and luxury items.
	Next 30 days continuous hospital confinement	**$219 each day**			
	Lifetime aggregate reserve of 60 additional days	**$438 each day**			
	After 150 days continuous hospital confinement	**100%**	Nothing		
Skilled Nursing Facilities: following hospital confinement.	First 20 days each benefit period*	**Nothing**	100% of covered charges	Must require skilled nursing or rehabilitation care within 30 days after hospital confinement that lasted at least 3 days.	Same as above; unskilled medical care (such as "Old Age Homes" and Custodial Care).
	Next 80 days continuous confinement	**$109.50 each day**	Balance		
	After 100 days continuous confinement each benefit period	**100%**	Nothing		
Home Health Care: by part-time visiting nurses, technicians, and therapists.	First 100 visits in spell of illness Part B covers any visits thereafter	**Nothing for covered charges; 20% of covered charges for durable medical equipment**	100% of covered services; 80% of covered amount for durable medical equipment	Must be home confined and physician must prescribe nursing/skilled care.	Full-time (private duty) nursing, homemaker services, self-administered drugs, services, covered under Part B.
Hospice Care	As long as the doctor certifies need	**Nothing†**	100% of covered services†	Must be terminally ill.	
Psychiatric Confinement Care	190-day lifetime limit		Same as Hospital Confinement with a lifetime maximum of 190 days.		
Overseas Hospital Care	No coverage	**100% of charges**	Nothing	Some coverage provided only in special circumstances.	

MEDICAL INSURANCE — PART B

Type of Service	Time Limit	Patient Risk	Medicare Pays	Qualifications	Exclusions
Physicians and Surgeons: services at home, hospital, or office. **Medical Services and Supplies:** diagnostic tests, surgical dressings, casts, splints, braces, artificial limbs and eyes, rental or purchase of medical equipment, ambulance, X-ray therapy, professionally administered drugs, some chiropractic services, nonroutine footcare. **Hospital Care:** Outpatient	No time limit	First $100 per calendar year, then 20% of "approved charges" *plus* any excess of charges over Medicare's "approved charges" if doctor or supplier does not accept assignment, up to limit.	Balance of "approved charges"	Voluntary enrollment, costs $66.60 per month plus 10% (per year) depending on date of enrollment, if you did not sign up when you were first eligible (workers and their spouses with employer group health coverage may delay enrollment and avoid the late enrollment penalty if they meet certain requirements).	Services covered by Workmens' Compensation, private duty nurses, eyeglasses, routine physicals, routine dental work, hearing aids, orthopedic shoes, nonskilled nursing care, cosmetic surgery, charges made by a relative, first three pints of blood in a calendar year, vaccinations, self-administered drugs, preventive care, services in a foreign country.
Home Health Care: part-time visiting nurses, aides, therapists.	Unlimited visits	Nothing	100% of approved charges	Same as for Part A home health care.	
Durable medical equipment.	Unlimited	20% of costs	80% of costs		Non-medical items.
Psychiatric Outpatient Care	Per calendar year	First $100, 50% of "allowable charges" plus excess of charges	You will ordinarily pay 50% of allowable charges. However, you will pay only 20% of allowable outpatient hospital charges if you would have required admission to the hospital without the treatment.		
Overseas Medical Care	No coverage	100% of charges	Nothing	Some coverage provided only in special circumstances in Canada and Mexico.	

* Each "benefit period" begins with the first day of hospital confinement and ends 60 days after having been discharged from a hospital or skilled nursing facility. If another hospital admission occurs after that, you must pay another deductible and the appropriate copays.

† You pay up to $5 for each prescription. Also, you pay 5% for the cost of respite care, not to exceed 5 consecutive days. There is no limit to the number of times you can get respite care.

Note: In all cases, services and supplies must be provided by Medicare-approved agencies or personnel, except in cases of emergency.

yond the Part B premium for this coverage. Others charge nothing extra, and some may even include payment of your Part B premium as a benefit of the plan.

Although Medicare managed-care plans are offered by private companies, you are still in the Medicare program. You will keep your Medicare rights and protections as well as receive the regular Medicare covered services. The options available under Medicare Advantage are discussed in Chapter V.

Medicare Part D

The Medicare program currently does not cover most prescription drugs, but this will soon change. In December 2003, President Bush signed the Medicare Prescription Drug, Improvement, and Modernization Act, which creates a new prescription drug benefit called Medicare Part D. The plan is voluntary and will be phased in over the next couple of years.

Beginning in May 2004, Medicare beneficiaries will be able to purchase a Medicare-approved drug discount card that will enable them to buy prescription drugs at a discount of 10 to 25 percent. Lower-income beneficiaries may qualify for a $600 credit on these cards to help pay for drugs.

Beginning in 2006, Medicare enrollees will have the option of purchasing prescription drug insurance. The plans may vary, but in general beneficiaries who choose to enroll will have to pay a premium and will be liable for an annual deductible and copayments, and Medicare will pay a share of their drug costs. This share will depend on how large your total out-of-pocket drug costs are. Beneficiaries with lower incomes and limited assets will be eligible for extra help.

The new Medicare prescription drug benefit is described in detail in Chapter III.

How Claims are Processed and Benefits are Paid

All Medicare participants are issued a Medicare card that contains a personal claim number that must be used whenever a claim is submitted. This card is the only evidence of Medicare insurance that most providers will accept, and Medicare will not pay any claims unless a claim number is provided. (If you are in a Medicare managed care plan, your membership card will have the name of the plan on it.)

Medicare claims usually are processed by third parties that have contracted with the government. For Medicare Part A, claims are processed by insurance companies or other organizations, such as Blue Cross/Blue Shield, that are known as "intermediaries." The hospital will submit charges directly to the intermediary, and the patient will be notified of any amounts that remain due (*i.e.*, the Medicare Part A deductible and charges for uncovered services) after Medicare has paid its benefits.

Medicare Part B claims are submitted directly by the physician who treats you to a "carrier" to be processed. If the physician agrees to accept what is known as "assignment," he or she will be paid according to Medicare's "approved charges" schedule and the patient will be billed only for the Medicare coinsurance amount (*i.e.*, the 20 percent not paid by Medicare). If the physician will not accept "assignment," the doctor's office still must submit a Medicare claim to the carrier in your behalf. The patient will then be billed for the Medicare coinsurance amount *plus* any excess physician's charges up to the Medicare-allowed maximum. Current Federal law limits these excess charges to 15 percent above the allowed charge. Some state laws limit excess charges even further.

Medicare also may be the "secondary payer" in certain cases where other insurance is in force. For example, if you have an automobile liability insurance policy that pays medical benefits for treatment of injuries sustained in an auto accident, a claim must be submitted to the automobile insurer and that policy's benefits must be paid before Medicare will pay any benefits. Medicare will pay the remainder of Medicare-covered charges as the "secondary payer" up to Medicare limits. Similarly, if you are employed past age 65, are enrolled in Medicare, and are also enrolled in an employer-sponsored health plan, Medicare will be the "secondary payer" with respect to Medicare-covered charges not covered by the employer-sponsored plan. Medicare also will be a "secondary payer" under such an employer-sponsored plan for a spouse age 65 or older. Claims and payments processing are considerably different with HMOs, described in Chapter V.

How Medicare Providers are Paid

Initially, Medicare reimbursed healthcare providers on a fee-for-

MEDICARE PART B USUALLY PROVIDES COVERAGE FOR:

Physician services

Hospital outpatient services

Physical therapy, speech pathology, and occupational therapy by physicians or institutional providers

Services of independent physical and occupational therapists, subject to limits

Macular degeneration treatment using ocular photodynamic therapy with verteporfin

Diagnostic x-ray, laboratory, and other tests

X-ray, radium, and radioactive therapy

Mammography screening

Second surgical opinions

Blood transfusions after the first three pints per year

Surgical dressings, splints, casts, etc., when ordered by a doctor

Necessary ambulance services

Rental (and in some cases purchase) of durable medical equipment for home use, when prescribed by a physician

Home health services (same as Part A)

Artificial replacements

Colostomy, ileostomy, and urostomy bags and supplies

Braces for limbs, back, or neck

Mental health services

service basis. That is, when a service was rendered, a bill was submitted for payment. However, since 1985, Medicare payments to hospitals have been made under the "Diagnosis Related Group" (DRG) system, which in most cases pays the hospital a fixed fee according to the diagnostic group (*i.e.*, illness) for which you are admitted, no matter how long you stay or what treatment is given. Changes have also been made in the terms of benefit payments to Medicare physicians. Under the Omnibus Budget Reconciliation Act of 1989 (OBRA), Medicare physicians are paid according to a fee schedule. This schedule is based on what Medicare authorities deem to be a "relative value scale" that pays physicians according to the number of years of training they have received, their overheads, and "geographical differences."

The Act also limits so-called excess charges, or what doctors may

MEDICARE PART B USUALLY PROVIDES *NO COVERAGE* FOR:

Acupuncture
Chiropractic services*
Christian Science practitioners' services*
Cosmetic surgery (except after an accident)
Custodial care
Dental care*
Experimental procedures
Eyeglasses (unless related to cataract surgery)
Foot care*
Foreign health care*
Hearing aids and examinations
Homemaker services
Immunizations except for pneumonia and infection*
Injections that can be self-administered
Meals delivered to your home
Naturopaths' services
Nursing care on full-time basis at home
Orthopedic shoes*
Personal convenience items
Physical examinations that are routine
Prescription drugs and medicines taken at home*
Preventive care
Private duty nurses
Private room*
Services performed by immediate relatives
Services not reasonable and necessary
Services payable by workers' compensation
Services or items for which you are not legally obligated to pay

* May be covered under special circumstances.

charge over and above the Medicare allowed fee. This last provision is of great significance, inasmuch as doctors' charges in excess of Medicare's approved fees usually have constituted one of the largest financial risks of Medicare beneficiaries. In effect, this legislation has reduced somewhat this category of risk. More recent federal and state legislation has restricted even further what doctors can charge in excess of the Medicare allowed fee.

The Importance of "Assignment"

If a doctor or other health care supplier accepts *assignment*, this simply means that he or she agrees to accept Medicare's "approved charges" as full payment. You will be responsible only for the $100 medical deductible plus additional coinsurance payments (the 20 percent of approved charges). Assignment does not mean that you have no liability, but it guarantees that a physician will not bill you for amounts beyond Medicare's approved charges. Assignment only applies to the services and supplies covered by Part B and works only within the "original" (fee-for-service) Medicare plan. Assignment does not apply if you are in a Medicare managed care plan (for example, an HMO).

Doctors and providers decide each year how they will handle assignment. Some of them always accept assignment (this means they "participate" in Medicare). Others accept assignment on a case-by-case basis, and still others never accept assignment.

Doctors and suppliers *must* accept assignment for lab tests covered by Medicare, for Medicaid patients whose states help pay their health care costs, and for Medicare-covered drugs and biologicals billed to a Durable Medical Equipment Regional Carrier under the durable medical equipment, prosthetics, orthotics, and supplies benefit. To find physicians or suppliers in your area who accept assignment call 1-800-MEDICARE (1-800-633-4227) or 1-877-486-2048 if you are hearing or speech impaired, or search the physician and supplier directories at Medicare's website, www.medicare.gov.

If you locate physicians who will accept assignment of fees, your financial risk can be effectively limited to the known Medicare deductible and coinsurance requirement for covered services. In these circumstances, Medicare supplemental insurance (a "medigap" policy) that restricts coverage to Medicare's coinsurance liability is adequate. You would be throwing money away by purchasing a policy that promises to pay more than 20 percent of Medicare's approved charges.

However, financial risk is the *least* of your risks in the event of life-threatening illness. You must be satisfied with the quality of health care you receive and you may not always wish to be treated by doctors who accept assignment. Top-flight specialists, for example, often charge fees that are beyond those approved by Medicare and, as discussed below, in such cases patient financial risk can be substantial. Federal law restricts doctors who do not accept assignment but who do provide services to patients who will be billed through

Medicare from charging more than 15 percent above Medicare's approved charge. However, some states have even lower limits. Other specialists may not agree to any Medicare participation whatsoever, and require a private fee-for-services contract. Currently there is no limit on fee schedules agreed to under such private contracts.

For more information on assignment, call the numbers above and ask for a free copy of Publication 10134, *Medicare & You: Does Your Doctor or Supplier Accept "Assignment?"* This publication is also available at Medicare's website.

"Participating" Doctors

Medicare maintains a list of physicians who "participate" in Medicare, meaning that they always accept "assignment" on Medicare-covered claims (as discussed above). This "Participating Physician Directory" is searchable online at www.medicare.gov and is a valuable resource for finding doctors by name, region, or specialty. It contains detailed information on each doctor, such as specialties, board certification, medical school, and hospital affiliation.

Medicare administrators frequently point to the high rate of physician "participation" as proof that seniors have adequate access to care. This claim, however, is misleading. Beneficiaries in some areas may find that, whereas many physicians may be listed as "participating," few—if any—may be accepting *new* Medicare patients. On the other hand, many "non-participating" physicians may be accepting new Medicare patients.

Confusing? Probably. The term "participating," in Medicare parlance, has nothing to do with patient access. Rather, it describes a mechanism of payment. "Participating" physicians agree to accept assignment on all Medicare claims and covered services and receive their payment directly from Medicare. "Non-participating" physicians, in contrast, can charge a higher rate, but must collect their fees from the patient.

With Medicare reimbursements rates being slashed and legally capped, patients are quickly learning that "participating" doesn't imply access.

Medicare's "Allowable Charge"

Medicare pays only its "allowed charges," not what a doctor may actually charge. In 2003, Medicare paid 80 percent of *allowable charges* after the $100 deductible was paid by the patient. If your doctor accepts assignment, this is your maximum financial risk. However, if your doctor does not accept assignment, your financial risk is higher.

Three different figures are used to arrive at the "allowable charge": (1) the customary charge, (2) the prevailing charge, and (3) the actual charge. As defined by Medicare, the *customary charge* is "generally the charge most frequently made by each doctor and supplier for each separate service or supply furnished to patients in the previous calendar year." The *prevailing charge* is "the amount which is high enough to cover the customary charges in three out of every four bills submitted in the previous year for each service and supply." The *actual charge* is what you are billed by the doctor or hospital. When a claim reaches Medicare, the "approved charge" is the lowest of these three amounts. In practice, the actual charge is almost never the lowest.

Medicare Does Not Travel Abroad

If you travel out of the country during your retirement years, you should arrange for payment of hospital and medical care in the event of illness. Except in three very restrictive situations, Medicare covers neither hospital costs nor medical costs abroad.

The special circumstances under which Medicare might provide coverage are:

1. You are in the United States when an emergency occurs and the closest hospital available to treat you is in Mexico or Canada. For example, if you are traveling close to either border and become ill, you are covered for care in a Mexican or Canadian hospital if it were the closest hospital to handle your emergency.

2. Your home in the United States is closer to a Canadian or Mexican hospital than a U.S. hospital. In this case, you are covered for both emergency and non-emergency care.

3. You are traveling from Alaska by the most direct route to another state. Medicare will cover emergency medical costs for treatment in Canada.

Most, but not all, Medicare supplemental insurance policies and

Medicare Advantage plans, such as HMOs, provide coverage for emergency health care in foreign countries.

Other Uncovered Services

As the table on page 21 suggests, traditional Medicare still does not cover many other health care services—and some of these may be costly. In short, there is a "medigap" that requires beneficiaries to either purchase a supplementary insurance policy, enroll in a Medicare Advantage plan, or use their savings to pay for health costs in excess of what Medicare pays for.

Part 2 of this book discusses currently available options for protecting yourself. First, however, let us turn to the latest effort by lawmakers to address a long-standing gap in Medicare, the absence of prescription drug coverage. As discussed in the next chapter, seniors soon will have new options for protecting themselves against high out-of-pocket expenses for such drugs.

III.

THE NEW MEDICARE
PRESCRIPTION DRUG BENEFIT

THE new Medicare law signed by President Bush in 2003 is the biggest expansion of Medicare since the program was created nearly 40 years ago. Officially titled the Medicare Prescription Drug, Improvement, and Modernization Act, it will add a voluntary prescription drug benefit to Medicare in 2006.

The new law is complicated and many questions remain about how it will work and what it will cost. With details still emerging and the major drug benefit not scheduled to take effect until 2006, its full consequences for seniors, taxpayers, and the health-care system will not become evident for some time. Whether or not it is a "good deal" for seniors will depend on their individual circumstances. The following is a review of the law's major provisions regarding drug coverage and other aspects of Medicare.

Drug Discount Card

Beginning in May 2004, Medicare beneficiaries will have the option of buying a drug discount card for about $30 per year. The cards will be offered by "sponsors" whose plans are endorsed by Medicare, and individuals will have at least two sponsors to choose from. They generally will be able to change plans only once each year. The Bush administration estimates that the card will yield savings of 10 percent or more off the price of covered prescription drugs, but actual savings remain to be seen and will vary from plan to plan.

According to *Consumer Reports* magazine, seniors who carefully comparison shop for low prescription drug prices can save more money than they can through existing drug discount cards. With that in mind, there may be little or no savings from the Medicare discount

---

MEDICARE DRUG COVERAGE CALCULATOR

To see what portion of your drug costs will be covered if you sign up for the Medicare prescription drug benefit when it begins in 2006, please see our Medicare Drug Coverage Calculator at www.aier.org/.

---

card for many older consumers. However, there is an additional benefit for low-income enrollees. Those with incomes below 135 percent of the Federal poverty guideline, or about $12,100 for individuals and $16,400 for couples, will get an annual credit of $600 embedded in their cards.

Main Drug Benefit

Beginning in 2006, Medicare beneficiaries will have the option of signing up for prescription drug coverage through either a stand-alone drug plan or a Medicare HMO plan that includes drug coverage.

In 2006, the "standard coverage" calls for beneficiaries to be responsible for the first $250 in drug costs. Medicare will pay 75 percent of the next $2,000 in drug costs. There will be no coverage for drug costs between $2,250 and $5,100 (this is the "donut hole"). Once beneficiaries spend $3,600 of their own money on drugs ($5,100 in total prescription-drug spending), Medicare will pay 95 percent of the rest of their drug costs. Thus, enrollees will be protected against catastrophically high out-of-pocket outlays for drugs, a remote but real risk.

To encourage competition, the drug benefit will not be provided by Medicare but by various sponsors, such as health insurance companies and pharmaceutical-benefit management companies. The legislation requires every Medicare beneficiary to have a choice of at least two plans to choose from. However, only one of these is required to be a stand-alone drug plan. Thus, in some regions (particularly rural areas), beneficiaries might have a "choice" of only one stand-alone drug benefit and a Medicare HMO (that, unlike standard fee-for-service Medicare, may restrict their choice of doctors and hospitals).

Each Plan Will Have Its Own Formulary

Benefits will vary from plan to plan. Each plan will have its own "formulary," or list of drugs that are covered. The law requires each formulary to include drugs within each "therapeutic category and class" of drugs, but not necessarily all drugs within each category. Thus, some beneficiaries may find that a drug their doctor recommends is not covered by a plan. Benefits may also vary if some plans offer more than standard coverage. The law allows them to offer "supplemental" coverage, such as reductions in the annual deductible or the 25 percent

28

copayments or the limit on out-of-pocket outlays.

Drug prices also will vary from plan to plan. The bill prohibits Medicare from negotiating prices with drug companies, but it allows each plan to do so. Currently, seniors who have no prescription drug coverage pay some of the highest retail prices in the country. Through the new Medicare benefit they will pay the (presumably lower) prices negotiated by plans. Keep in mind that many large benefit plans should be able to negotiate significant volume discounts. For example, AARP has more members than the total population of Canada.

The Bush administration estimates that the premium for a standard drug plan will be about $35 per month in 2006 ($420 per year), but this is not guaranteed. Premiums may vary from plan to plan and region to region, and they probably will increase every year. For a given plan in a given region, the premium generally will be the same for all enrollees.

Initial Enrollment and Late Enrollment Penalties

Medicare beneficiaries who fail to sign up during an initial enrollment period will be subject to a late enrollment penalty if they choose to sign up later, unless they can show that they had other prescription drug coverage through a retiree plan, veterans' benefits, etc. The idea is to discourage healthy seniors who currently have no other drug coverage from waiting "until they need it" to enroll. (For any insurance plan to work, it is essential to enroll people who "don't need it yet." Their premiums provide revenue that helps cover the cost of claims.)

A Better Deal for Some Seniors

Older beneficiaries – people who are now in their 70s, 80s, and 90s – who have no other drug coverage and enroll when the program begins in 2006 will get a better "deal" than younger seniors. They can enroll on the same terms as everyone else, whereas people who turn 65 in 2006 or later who delay enrollment until, say, their 70s or 80s will face late enrollment penalties; their monthly premium will be increased by at least one percent for every month they delay enrollment.

The Deductible and Limits are Indexed

One little-noted provision of the plan is that the $250 deductible and the limits on out-of-pocket outlays will probably increase every year. They are indexed to the annual increase in the per-capita cost of the program. This adjustment could be large if the recent trends of rising drug prices and increased usage persist. In a nutshell, this means that the deductible and the limit on out-of-pocket outlays could rapidly escalate. For example, if per-capita drug outlays were to increase by five percent per year (a conservative scenario), over a period of five years the annual deductible would increase from $250 to $325 and the limit on out-of-pocket outlays would rise from $3,600 to $4,600.

Seniors will not be able to rely on Medicare supplemental insurance (medigap) policies to fill these coverage gaps. If the market were allowed to operate freely, insurance companies might have modified their existing policies to do just this. But the law prohibits the sale or renewal of medigap policies that include coverage for these particular gaps to seniors who enroll in the new Medicare drug plan. The hope is that requiring seniors to pay some of their drug costs out of pocket will give them a stronger incentive to keep costs (and the government's share of those costs) down.

Low-Income Subsidies

The premium, deductible, and coverage gap will be waived for people with incomes below 135 percent of the Federal poverty guideline. To qualify for the subsidy, seniors may have no more than $6,000 in assets, other than a house, a car, and a few other limited assets. The subsidies would be phased out for incomes between 135 percent and 150 percent of the poverty guideline (currently about $12,100 to $13,500).

Medicare beneficiaries who are also covered by Medicaid, the Federal-state health program for poor people that already covers drugs, will now have their drug costs picked up by Medicare. In addition, a few million seniors whose incomes are too high to qualify for Medicaid will qualify for the low-income subsidy for the new Medicare benefit.

Retiree Coverage

The percentage of employers offering retiree health benefits has fallen significantly in recent years. For example, in 1988, 66 percent of all large firms (with 200 or more workers) offered retiree health coverage, compared with just 38 percent in 2003. The Medicare bill provides tax-free subsidies, perhaps worth as much as $70 billion, to employers who maintain prescription drug coverage for retirees after the Medicare drug benefit begins in 2006. Even so, the trend of companies dropping their retiree health coverage is expected to continue.

Medicare Part B Premium

Under current law, most Medicare beneficiaries pay the same premium for Part B (Medical Insurance). These premiums, currently $66.60 per month, are supposed to cover 25 percent of the cost of the program, although in recent years this share has been smaller. The rest of Part B is paid for with general tax revenue, and Medicare Part A (Hospital Insurance) is financed primarily through the payroll tax. Thus, only a small portion of total Medicare costs is paid for by beneficiaries. And in the current system, low-income workers pay taxes to cover the benefits of seniors who may be far wealthier than they are.

The new law takes a small step toward making wealthy seniors pay more. Beginning in 2007, Part B premiums will be means-tested for the first time. Individuals with incomes greater than $80,000 ($160,000 for couples) will pay a larger premium. The size of their premium will increase on a sliding scale tied to their income, reaching a maximum for seniors with incomes above $200,000. In addition, for all seniors the deductible for Part B will rise from $100 to $110 in 2005 and thereafter be indexed to the growth in Part B spending.

Role of Private Companies

A number of changes are designed to spur competition in Medicare. As noted, private firms will administer the drug benefit on a regional basis. The bill will also provide $12 billion in subsidies to encourage more private insurers to offer Medicare Advantage health plans. These include Medicare HMOs as well as preferred-provider organizations (PPOs), and private fee-for-service plans, which allow patients to see any doctor.

Beginning in 2010, traditional Medicare also will face competition from private plans in a few selected regions. In six metropolitan areas in which at least two private plans (for example, Medicare HMOs) enroll at least 25 percent of Medicare beneficiaries, the costs of the private plans and of traditional fee-for-service would be compared. If traditional Medicare costs more, seniors who chose to remain in it would pay higher premiums. Their premium increases would be capped at five percent a year and waived for low-income seniors. This "demonstration project" is scheduled to last for six years.

It remains to be seen whether private Medicare plans can succeed, but history is not encouraging. Dozens of Medicare HMOs dropped their plans in the past decade, partly because their reimbursements from Medicare were too low. Financing questions aside, it may be difficult for private plans to gain the trust of the Medicare population, after millions of beneficiaries lost their HMO coverage in the past decade and were forced to return to traditional coverage.

Competition—providing people with a choice—is a good thing. But the evidence suggests that people value the right to choose their doctors and hospitals more than the right to choose among health plans.

Drugs from Canada

The bill maintains the ban on importing prescription drugs. It would allow such drugs from Canada, but only if the Health and Human Services Department certifies their safety, something it has declined to do. The legislation authorizes a study of safety issues.

Safety is a legitimate concern, but there is no good reason why it cannot be addressed through a combination of regulation and market forces. That is how Americans successfully import other potentially unsafe goods. Americans currently pay the highest prices in the world for their drugs, because other countries have national health care systems that negotiate price discounts. As long as this discrepancy persists, there will be pressure to reduce prices here or to allow Americans to import cheaper drugs.

Summary

For all the debate over the need for Medicare prescription drug coverage, it is unclear how many seniors need it and how popular this plan will be. Many retirees already have other coverage through their former employers, although there is a growing risk that their coverage may be reduced or eliminated.

The Medicare drug plan is an attempt to balance government benefits with market incentives. It is different from the type of Medicare coverage with which most people are familiar, or the coverage many people have during their working years. Unlike many employer-sponsored drug plans that provide first-dollar coverage and a uniform copayment for every drug purchase, the Medicare plan is more of a catastrophic insurance plan designed to make the beneficiary a stakeholder in controlling costs. Even this limited benefit will cost seniors and taxpayers a great deal. There is no getting around the fact that adding drug coverage to Medicare is bound to be expensive, no matter who pays for it.

The winners and losers will become clearer once the new plans become available in 2006. Clearly, it will be important for seniors to conduct careful research before they decide whether or not to enroll in the new drug benefit. Unfortunately, if a mistake is made during the open enrollment period (*e.g.*, deciding to do nothing), it could prove costly at a later date.

Healthy seniors with no other drug coverage may be tempted to postpone signing up if their drug expenses currently are small. But the penalty for late enrollment will discourage this if it is sufficiently large. If they do enroll, some will no doubt find themselves paying more in premiums and copayments than they receive in benefits. But they will be protected against financially catastrophic drug costs – a remote but real risk.

IV.

WHY YOU NEED "MEDIGAP" PROTECTION

FOR any illness, there will be immediate costs. You will have to visit the doctor at least once or twice. Furthermore, if the condition requires it, you will have to be hospitalized for a day or two. These initial costs, which are predictable and inevitable with most illnesses, are termed "front-end" costs by the insurance companies. They apply to the early stages of treatment, and your personal liability for them usually corresponds to your Medicare deductibles. If these were the only costs that Medicare enrollees faced, they would have little need for "medigap" insurance or the additional protection provided by Medigap Advantage plans (such as HMOs).

"Tail-end" costs, on the other hand, refer to those expenses that occur toward the end of an illness or remain *after* traditional Medicare has paid all its benefits. Unlike the initial costs of an illness, the tail-end costs are virtually unpredictable. Standard Medicare does not cover them, and if they are not protected against, they can lead to financial ruin. Extended hospital confinements, although rare, can easily run into tens and often hundreds of thousands of dollars.

Many insurance policies and HMOs cover both front-end and tail-end costs. But many others offer an option, for example, reduced tail-end coverage in return for front-end coverage. When presented with this option, **always choose the best tail-end coverage**. The later stages of hospital and medical care have the greatest financial risks. Front-end costs occur more often but they are more financially manageable. Tail-end costs are by far the largest part of the "medigap."

Any Medicare supplemental insurance policy or Medicare Advantage plan that you purchase should, first and foremost, cover the two categories of tail-end costs that pose the greatest risk to Medicare patients: (1) the costs of catastrophic illness that may continue after Medicare Part A benefits run out and (2) the costs that remain after Medicare Part B has paid its 80 percent of "approved charges."

More generally, as the discussion of Medicare in Chapter II suggests, there is a broader "medigap" that leaves you exposed to financial risk for a range of services and items that are not covered by standard Medicare. Part 2 of this book discusses the options available to beneficiaries to protect themselves against these risks.

As you review these options, keep in mind that to purchase a medigap insurance policy, you must be covered under both Part A and Part B of the Medicare program. You have a 6-month open-enrollment period (that begins with the first month that you are age 65 or over and also enrolled in Medicare) to buy the policy of your choice. **During this period, you cannot be denied coverage or charged a higher price because of current or past health prob-**

QUICKER & SICKER?

Under Medicare Part A, Medicare's payments to hospitals are made under the "Diagnosis Related Group" (DRG) prospective payment system. As discussed earlier in Chapter II, in most cases this means that Medicare pays the hospital a fixed fee for treatment of a specified illness. The implementation of this DRG system in 1985 may itself have introduced a new "health risk" to Medicare patients. Medicare officials have become alarmed at reported instances of premature release of patients—that is, where hospitals release patients "quicker & sicker." Therefore, they now require hospitals to inform Medicare patients of their legal right to challenge their discharge from a hospital if they or their physicians believe such discharge is premature. *If the hospital does not notify you of your rights and you decide to stay after your discharge date, you can't be charged for the cost of your care.*

"Dumping" of Medicare patients whose hospital stay exceeds the DRG patient allowance for their diagnosis is a predictable result of the prospective payment system. Whether wittingly or unwittingly, hospital officials in a number of reported cases have informed their Medicare patients that their "Medicare hospital benefits have run out" and that therefore the hospital must discharge them.

Understand that *the prospective payment system does not limit your stay in the hospital to the time corresponding to the reimbursement provided by any diagnosis related group.* Your benefits cannot "run out" before your discharge is clinically warranted. As a Medicare patient, you have a right to appeal your discharge to the local medical peer review organization. That organization must issue a decision within 3 days of receiving your appeal, and the hospital cannot force you to leave before then.

---

lems. (The insurer may make you wait for up to six months before it pays benefits for pre-existing conditions, but it cannot turn you down.) If you do not enroll during this period, you may not be able to get the policy you want, or you may be charged a higher premium. **You do not need to buy a medigap policy if you are in a Medicare managed care plan, or if you are covered by Medicaid.**

Beyond this legal protection, the National Association of Insurance Commissioners (NAIC) has developed model standards for ten Medicare Supplemental Insurance policies. Insurance companies are

---

If your appeal is granted, you may stay in the hospital and it must absorb any cost of your treatment that exceeds the DRG reimbursement amount.

If your appeal is denied, you still cannot be charged for the days of your hospitalization that follow the hospital's notification of its intent to discharge you and prior to the peer review organization's decision, which should be no more than 3 days.

Although one would expect that in most cases of attempted premature discharge, your attending physician would offer full support of any warranted appeal you may make (or actually initiate it), be aware that the prospective payment system has imposed disincentives to such appeals by physicians: even if a doctor follows the guidelines set by a peer review panel to admit or retain a patient, the same panel can later disallow the stay and reimbursement. Peer review panels are primarily engaged in slashing expenses, and any physician who interferes with a review organization's task of cutting costs risks being labeled a "Medicare abuser" and losing hospital privileges.

Thus, it is your responsibility to initiate the appeal process if, after consultation with your physician, you feel that you are being discharged prematurely.

When you are admitted to a Medicare participating hospital, you should be given a copy of *An Important Message From Medicare*. It explains your rights as a hospital patient. If you are not given one, ask for it. The message explains what to do if you think the hospital is making you leave too soon. If you have questions about this, call the Quality Improvement Organization (QIO). Their number is on the message.

FINDING A DOCTOR

Medicare maintains a list of physicians who "participate" in Medicare, meaning that they accept the program's "approved charges" as full payment for Medicare-covered claims. This "Participating Physician Directory," which is searchable online at www.medicare.gov, is a valuable resource for finding doctors by name, region, or specialty.

The directory contains detailed information on each doctor, such as specialties, board certification, medical school, and hospital affiliation. It also includes their phone numbers and addresses. The list is not comprehensive, because not all doctors "participate" in Medicare. But it is a helpful starting point for finding out more about physicians, particularly the training and certification information that is so important but often difficult to find.

You can verify whether a doctor is board certified by calling the American Board of Medical Specialties at 1-866-ASK-ABMS (866-275-2267). This information is also available online at www.abms.

not required to offer all ten policies, but any policies they do offer must provide the coverage specified by these standards. Chapter VII discusses these policies in detail.

Medicare coverage has been subject to frequent change. And each time Medicare's coverage has changed, the terms of coverage of the various medigap policies then in force have also changed. Medicare administrators base their premium decisions and claims payment practices on existing legislation, and these too are subject to change. Although it may be unsettling, virtually all health insurance decisions that today's senior citizens face should be made with the understanding that they probably will be temporary ones.

Part 2
HOW TO PROTECT YOURSELF
AGAINST THE "MEDIGAP"

V.

MEDICARE ADVANTAGE PLANS

FOR some years, Medicare beneficiaries with both Part A and Part B coverage have had the option of choosing, subject to availability, to sign up for a variety of private market-based health care plans (such as HMOs) similar to those available to the non-Medicare population. Congress has tried to make these plans more widely available by enacting various bills to fund and promote them. In 1997, for example, it created the Medicare + Choice (Part C) program, which, on paper, greatly expanded the choices of Medicare enrollees. In practice, the program had only limited success.

The Medicare law signed by President Bush in 2003 is another attempt to provide more choice. The new law changes the name of Medicare + Choice to Medicare Advantage. (It is still Part C of the Medicare program). It also provides $12 billion in subsidies to persuade private insurers to remain, enter or re-enter the Medicare managed care program.

Medicare beneficiaries may still opt for just the original fee-for-service plan run by the Federal government. You pay the Part B premium ($66.60 per month in 2004), the Part A and Part B deductibles, and any fees for services not fully covered by Medicare. You have access to any doctor that accepts Medicare and you receive the basic Part A and Part B services discussed in Chapter II.

As explained in that chapter, the original fee-for-service plan entails significant financial risks because Medicare does not cover all medical expenses. Medigap insurance, discussed in Chapter VII, is one way to protect yourself against these risks. Medicare Advantage (Part C) is also intended to reduce those risks. **You do not need to buy a medigap policy if you are in a Part C plan or if you are covered by Medicaid.**

Part C options include several managed care arrangements—health maintenance organizations (HMOs), HMOs with point of service (POS) options, provider sponsored organizations (PSOs), preferred provider organizations (PPOs)—and nonmanaged-care, private fee-for-service (PFFS) plans. The availability of these plans varies widely across the country. In some states, a large percentage of Medicare

41

beneficiaries are enrolled in HMOs and the like, but in other states no such plans are even offered.

Health Maintenance Organizations (HMOs)

HMOs began serving Medicare beneficiaries in 1982, predating the Medicare + Choice program by 15 years. In 2001, more than 5.5 million beneficiaries were enrolled in 179 HMOs across the country.

Like all managed care plans, HMOs in theory provide health care more efficiently than conventional fee-for-service arrangements. Under what is now called the "original Medicare plan," Medicare pays doctors and other health care providers directly for each service a patient receives. Under managed care health plans, however, Medicare pays a lump sum, called the *capitation rate*, to the plan administrator who in turn manages the services you receive. The administrator contracts directly with hospitals and other health care providers, paying them a predetermined amount based on the number of patients they serve and the types of services they provide, rather than a fee based on the actual costs of providing these services. If the providers' costs exceed the predetermined payment, they lose money. Thus, participating hospitals and doctors have greater incentives to keep costs down.

Therefore, under managed care, your out-of-pocket costs (premiums and copayments) usually are lower. Moreover, beneficiaries do not have to contend with burdensome paperwork or the irregularities of Medicare's "approved charges" schedule. HMOs have no pre-existing illness clauses, waiting periods, or elimination periods. Members generally are entitled to full coverage as soon as they enroll.

HMOs generally provide better coverage than conventional fee-for-service arrangements. Federally-certified HMOs must offer all services covered by Medicare and must meet minimum protection standards prescribed for supplemental health insurance policies. Most HMOs offer plans that also pay for things that Medicare does not, such as routine physical examinations, immunizations, routine eye examinations, hearing aid examinations, and dental care. Some of the lower-cost "basic" packages have dropped eye, hearing, and dental coverage in recent years. However, benefits may soon become *more* generous because the 2003 Medicare law provided additional funds to Medicare health plans.

Some Part C plans charge no premium to beneficiaries, beyond the standard Medicare Part B premium. However, the percentage of Medicare beneficiaries with access to zero-premium Part C plans declined dramatically from 61 percent in 1999 to 32 percent in 2002. Moreover, during that period, the percentage of Medicare patients with access to a Part C plan with drug coverage also declined, from 65 percent to 50 percent.

Be aware, then, that your choice of an HMO plan will affect your costs, what extra benefits you receive, and how much choice you have among doctors, specialists, and hospitals. It will affect your access to care and the quality of your care. And beware that any plan's benefits and costs are subject to change from year to year, and that Medicare health plans are free to terminate their contract with Medicare at the end of each calendar year. *More than two million Medicare beneficiaries have been dropped by Medicare HMO plans since 1998, leaving many with no choice but to return to the original Medicare program.*

HMOs with a Point of Service (POS) Option

HMOs with a point-of-service (POS) option, originally called "open-ended HMOs," have been around since 1961. Members can choose to use the HMO network or to go outside the network each time they need care. If they choose to use the network, their primary-care physicians coordinate the care.

From a purely financial standpoint, it is always in the member's best interest to use the network. However, from a health care standpoint, it may make sense to go outside the network for certain care. With the POS option, members can go to the provider of choice *without coordination or approval* of the primary care physician or so-called gatekeeper. Claims for out-of-network care, usually much larger than in-network copays, are reimbursed after any applicable deductible and coinsurance provisions are met. Furthermore, non-network providers may charge much more than the network's reimbursement levels.

POS plans are best suited for people who would generally stay within the HMO network for most of their routine care but value the freedom to go out-of-network if a major illness strikes. In essence, the POS option acts as a (costly) safety valve.

43

Preferred Provider Organizations (PPOs)

Preferred Provider Organizations (PPOs) consist of hospitals and physicians who agree to provide services at negotiated fees. Third-party payers, such as insurance companies or large employers, can access the network to provide health care services for covered individuals. The PPO charges an access fee that varies with the services used and does not generally require members to choose a primary-care doctor or remain in-network as do HMOs.

Like HMO plans with a point-of-service option, PPOs are best suited to people who plan to stay "in-network" for most of their health care services but who do not want to be permanently "locked-in" to a particular network of doctor or hospitals or who do not always want to obtain permission from a primary care physician to see a specialist.

Provider-Sponsored Organizations (PSOs)

Provider-Sponsored Organizations (PSOs), as the name suggests, consist of doctors and hospitals that have formed their own plans. The providers themselves, not insurance companies, run the plan. An important question is how large the network of participating doctors is in a particular plan. While some metropolitan-area PSOs have grown into large conglomerates of providers offering extensive services, PSO caregiver networks are often more limited than either HMOs or PPOs. It would seem crucial in such cases that enrollees be permitted to seek treatment outside the PSO in a manner similar to PPOs and HMOs with a point-of-service option. If not, patient choice could be severely limited.

Plan Choices May Expand in 2006

Medicare Advantage plans are unavailable in many areas of the country, particularly rural areas. And where they are available, enrollees often are restricted to their plan's local service area for most non-emergency health care. However, the recent Medicare legislation calls for the establishment of "regional preferred provider organizations (PPOs)" in 2006. These plans will be offered to beneficiaries in yet-to-be-determined regions, each of which will cover at least one state. The Secretary of Health and Human Resources is conducting research to determine how the 10 to 50 regions should be created. Although much remains to be seen about how these plans will work, the goal is to ensure that all Medicare beneficiaries have at least one Medicare Advantage plan to choose from as an alternative to regular Medicare.

Disadvantages of HMOs

A major disadvantage of HMOs is that members are generally limited to care under participating physicians and hospitals. Many plans claim they have a large pool of member physicians, and often their prospectuses list all physicians who participate in their program. By implication, HMO members are free to choose their care providers from a large number of clinical personnel. In practice, the number of participating doctors may be deceptive. Very often, the most sought-after physicians already are "fully subscribed." Hence, even though the total number of physicians in the HMO may be quite large, the proportionately few who may accept *new* patients may be the relatively inexperienced practitioners.

Before you join an HMO, you should determine which HMO physicians are available to *new* members. If you are not satisfied with that list of doctors, you should go elsewhere.

If you become dissatisfied with your doctor, you can change to another within the organization. But you still are limited to care under HMO physicians who are accepting new patients. This rule does not apply if you require a specialist who is not in the plan. In this case, HMO physicians will refer you to several specialists, and the HMO may pay the costs of whomever you select. If an illness requires major surgery, it normally must be performed in an HMO-participating hospital. You are free to choose your own surgeon, but if you elect to have surgery performed elsewhere, you likely will have to pay the entire bill yourself unless you have a POS option.

To date, there have been relatively few studies published on HMO quality-of-care. In the past, the cost-cutting measures of managed care have reportedly led to numerous abuses and inconveniences for members: long waiting times for appointments, tests, and treatment; repeated shifting of patient assignments (you may not see the same doctor from one visit to the next); lack of concern for patient welfare; and reluctance to proceed with high-cost treatment or referrals to specialists outside the plan even when it is clinically warranted.

However, most patients indicate overall satisfaction with the care they receive. Large majorities of beneficiaries report visiting their usual doctor, and of those, 95 percent (in one study) say they were either satisfied or very satisfied with their care. Those with a usual place of care, but not a usual doctor, were somewhat less satisfied. At the same time, it is interesting that *voluntary* disenrollments from Medicare Part C plans have been rising along with involuntary disenrollments, and that almost half of those leaving on their own are exiting managed care altogether and returning to traditional Medicare.

At a minimum, you should carefully investigate the plans you are thinking of joining. Check the credentials of any doctor you are considering as a "primary care provider." In some states, the state medical board will tell you if a doctor is licensed, has been sued for malpractice, has been disciplined, or has received complaints. Ask friends and neighbors about the HMO physicians. Call or visit the doctors you are most interested in and ask the questions that are most important to you. For example, will they advise you over the phone on common medical problems? Do they treat other patients with your problem?

Find out as much as you can about participating hospitals—all hospitals are not created equal. How well does the staff treat people with your condition? (Providers are more successful the more they perform a procedure.) Do many patients get infections? Talk to plan members. Are they satisfied with the care they have been getting? Have their complaints been addressed? Would they join the HMO now, given their knowledge of its operations?

For many helpful contacts and suggestions on selecting physicians and hospitals, call Medicare and ask for copies of *Choosing a Doctor* and *Choosing a Hospital*. These guides were developed jointly by Medicare and the Agency for Healthcare Research and Quality. You may also download them from Medicare's website (www.medicare.gov).

You can also obtain information about the quality of plans in your area from Medicare's website using the "Medicare Personal Plan Finder." More information regarding this helpful tool is provided later in this chapter. Here, it is sufficient to note that you can use it to evaluate the health plans in your area (assuming such plans are available—in many areas of the country there are no alternatives to original Medicare). The information in the "Finder" was collected from both the managed care plans themselves and directly from individuals enrolled in the plans, and has been checked for accuracy by Medicare. Currently, the information is updated through the year 2002. Here is a sampling of the statistics you will find (given in percentages on the website):

- Members who said they always got care when they needed it without long waits

- Those who rated their own care as the best possible

- Members who said the plan doctors always communicate well

- Beneficiaries who did not have problems getting referred to a specialist

- Those who rated their own plan as the best possible plan

As a rule of thumb, when measuring quality, a difference of ten percentage points between plans' scores on a particular measure indicates a significant difference.

If you have determined that the quality of medical services provided by an HMO meets your criteria, you still must be concerned about its financial health. Mismanagement has landed a number of plans in financial difficulty. Medicare regulations require that defunct HMOs continue to provide coverage for Medicare subscribers for six months after bankruptcy is declared, after which time your coverage ends, potentially disrupting your medical care.

While the government protects you somewhat in the event you lose your Medicare Advantage coverage due to no fault of your own, *there can be no guarantee that your doctor participates in any of the alternative Medicare programs, including the original program.* Citing insufficient payments from the government, increasing numbers of doctors are dropping Medicare patients or refusing to accept new ones.

As many as two-thirds of the country's HMOs have at times operated in the red, and many of these could be sold or merged with other organizations. Therefore, try to determine the financial status of an HMO before joining. In addition to requesting a copy of the plan's most recent financial statement, you should ask a plan representative:

- How many of the HMO's physicians have left during the past five years? If there has been a "mass exodus" of doctors, you want to know why. Try to interview any such physicians.

- Is it an independent financial entity or part of a larger organization (HMO chain)? If it is part of a larger chain, ask to see the annual report of the parent group.

- Is it owned by an insurance company? If so, check that company's financial statements. If the HMO is taking losses, the company may try to sell or dismantle it.

- Is the Medicare segment of the HMO reporting losses? If so, are there plans to cancel membership for Medicare recipients?

How to Double Check an HMO's Financial Status

If HMO representatives are reluctant to answer your questions or do not provide you with the materials you request, do not do further business with them. If they provide answers, you still should double check the accuracy of their statements.

Two major rating agencies that rate the financial condition of HMOs are the A.M. Best Company and Weiss Ratings. Their published financial reports and ratings may be available in the reference section of your local library. You can also find information on their websites: the A.M. Best Company site is www.ambest.com; and the Weiss Ratings site is www.weissratings.com. For more information on these ratings, see Chapter VIII.

Weiss Ratings is the more consumer-oriented agency, and historically its ratings have been among the most accurate in the financial ratings industry. It rates the financial status of over 1,700 health insurance companies, 700 HMOs, and all of the Blue Cross Blue Shield plans. A rating for one HMO costs $19.00 over the phone or $15.99 for a one-page report purchased online. For more information, call (800) 289-9222 or go to their website.

Some HMO chains also are listed in the *Value Line Investment Survey*, a regularly updated survey that ranks the safety and financial performance of publicly traded stocks.

It is only common sense that Medicare recipients avoid any HMO

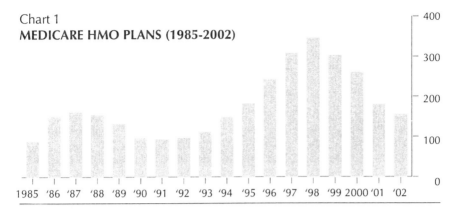

Chart 1
MEDICARE HMO PLANS (1985-2002)

1985 '86 '87 '88 '89 '90 '91 '92 '93 '94 '95 '96 '97 '98 '99 2000 '01 '02

that is likely to be liquidated or to cancel Medicare memberships. However, if you find an HMO that is well-established, financially strong, and clinically superior, membership may provide good value relative to that of conventional medigap insurance. Otherwise, it would seem prudent to forgo such membership until a more financially solid HMO becomes available.

The Medicare HMO Outlook

Enrollment in Medicare managed-care plans rose from 440,000 in 1985 to 1.8 million in 1993 to a peak of 6.3 million in 1999. However, since the inception of Part C in 1997, HMO participation in Medicare has fallen dramatically, from a high of 346 plans in 1998 to 155 plans in 2002 (see Chart 1). During this period, a total of 2.2 million Medicare beneficiaries lost HMO coverage due to plan withdrawals. In 2001 alone, withdrawals affected almost a million persons, or 14.7 percent of Part C enrollees. Clearly, *seniors have not been able to count on these plans.* Time will tell if the new Medicare Advantage will work better than Medicare + Choice did, and whether the additional government funding recently provided to these plans will stem the outflow of enrollees.

Losing Your Medicare HMO Coverage?

If your Medicare HMO or other Part C plan coverage terminates for one of the following reasons, you have the right to return to the original Medicare plan and purchase supplemental (medigap) insurance as described:

- If, when you first became eligible for Medicare at age 65, you

49

enrolled in a Medicare HMO and then disenrolled from that plan within 12 months of the effective date of your enrollment, you have the right to purchase, within 63 calendar days, any medigap policy sold in your state.

• If you join a Medicare HMO plan after you first become eligible for Medicare, drop your medigap policy, and subsequently disenroll from the HMO within the first year, you may return to your original policy if it is still available from the same insurance company, provided this was the first time you joined a Part C plan. Otherwise, you may purchase medigap policies A, B, C, or F (discussed in Chapter VII) if sold in your state. In either case, you must apply for your policy within 63 calendar days after your HMO coverage ends.

• If your Medicare HMO coverage ends because (1) your plan terminated its Medicare participation or stopped providing care in your area, (2) you moved outside the plan's service area, or (3) you left the plan because it failed to meet its contractual obligations, you have the right to purchase medigap policies A, B, C, or F that are sold in your state. You must apply for medigap within 63 calendar days of losing your coverage.

In each of the above cases, the insurance company cannot deny you the policy, place conditions on the policy such as a waiting period, apply a pre-existing condition exclusion, or discriminate in the price of the policy based on your health status. (Make sure you keep a copy of your plan's termination letter to prove that you lost coverage in a situation described above.)

Otherwise, should you *voluntarily* disenroll from a Medicare HMO or other Part C plan *one year or more after joining* and decide to return to the original Medicare plan and wish to purchase a medigap policy, you risk being subjected to medical underwriting standards. *The insurance company may deny your application or impose policy restrictions and charge you more because your health is unacceptable.* This is very important. Once you are enrolled in a Medicare HMO for more than a year, you may find it difficult or costly—if not impossible—to get a medigap policy should you then decide to disenroll from Medicare Part C.

The passage of the 2003 Medicare reform act may slow or reverse the steady stream of managed-care plans flowing out of Medicare since the inception of Part C, and actions by the remaining plans to water down benefits. In any event, these "guarantees" provide an important safety net for your medical coverage. However, as already noted, you must still be prepared for potential disruption of your health care, especially if your doctor or hospital does not participate in one of your alternative options or if the coverage you desire is not included in any of the plans.

If you are fortunate enough to live in an area with one or several Part C options, you may take advantage of another government guarantee: Under legislation signed by President Bush in June 2002, until 2005 you can enroll in any of the managed plans or private fee-for-service plans in your area at any time—provided the plan is accepting new members. In addition, *all* Medicare Advantage plans must be open to new members between November 15 and December 31. It does not matter how long you have been in Medicare or how long you have been in your current plan, if you have one. This legislation applies only if you are moving *into* Medicare Advantage from the original Medicare plan or from a medigap plan, or if you are moving *within* Medicare Advantage from plan to plan. The June 2002 legislation does not apply to beneficiaries *leaving* Medicare Advantage and returning to (or entering) the medigap market. In this case, the original guarantees, detailed above, apply. (You may elect to disenroll at any time and for any reason from most Medicare health plans. Simply write or call your plan, or call Medicare.)

The Medicare Personal Plan Finder

When Medicare was created 40 years ago, beneficiaries had few decisions to make about their Medicare coverage. Mainly they made choices about which doctor to go to and which treatment to get. As the Medicare system expands toward providing more choices among health plans (and, soon, prescription drug benefit plans) it is becoming increasingly important for beneficiaries to learn more about the changing options available to them.

Unlike Social Security, there are no Medicare offices available to answer your questions in person. It is up to you to conduct your own Medicare research, *before* you make any major decisions regarding health insurance. However, as noted earlier, Medicare does provide a service called the Medicare Personal Plan Finder to help you learn about the health plan choices available in your region.

The Medicare Personal Plan Finder can be reached through the Medicare website, by contacting a Medicare representative at 1-800-Medicare (1-800-633-4227), or by contacting an insurance counselor at your state health insurance and assistance program. The website is the fastest and, for many, the best way to access the information. Those without internet access at home or through a friend may find it worthwhile to visit their local library, community college, or senior center and ask for assistance in getting on the website. Or, if you are not in a hurry you can use the phone to get a personalized printed report that should be delivered by mail within three weeks.

The Medicare Personal Plan Finder provides a list of all of the health plan options available in your community, as well as information on the cost of each plan and the average out-of-pocket costs for someone of your age and health.

If you are mainly interested in a Medicare Advantage plan for its prescription drug benefit, keep in mind that the main drug benefit in the 2003 Medicare law will become available in 2006. Until then you can use the Medicare Personal Plan Finder to see if any Medicare Advantage plans in your region provide prescription drug coverage.

The value of any plan's drug benefit will be affected by the coverage caps, copayments, and how the price of a drug is applied to the cap (ask the plan). To determine the value of the drug benefit, first total your drug costs for the year, and then subtract the sum of the following items: the plan's copayments, the uncovered cost (cost after copayments less cap), and the annual plan premium. The larger this difference, the greater the benefit of the drug coverage. Note that owing to the rising cost of pharmaceuticals, many plans are raising premiums, raising copayments, lowering caps, paying only for drugs on an approved list (called the formulary), or some combination thereof.

Unfortunately, many of those who need help with Medicare are not aware that many helpful resources exist, and even when they think that help is available they have a difficult time finding it. The Medicare Personal Plan Finder is just one of many publications, services, and resources available from Medicare to help individuals make critical health, medical and financial decisions. (See the appendix for a list of these resources.)

Private Contracts

Perhaps the most controversial provision under Medicare Part C is the "private contracts option," which permits Medicare enrollees to contract privately, independent of Medicare, with physicians of their choosing. Medicare would pay none of the physician's charges and it would be the responsibility of the patient to negotiate fees under such contracts, unfettered by any price regulations.

Prior to Medicare + Choice, Medicare patients had long obtained medical services outside the Medicare program—both Medicare-covered services and services not covered by Medicare. However, confusion arose as to whether "excess fee restrictions" imposed by Federal and state law applied to Medicare-covered services delivered outside the Medicare program. The original intent of adding the private-contracting option to the Medicare + Choice legislation, according to the bill's sponsors, was to make it explicit that Medicare patients had the right to contract privately with a doctor of their choice for medical services for which no claim for payment is submitted to Medicare—regardless of whether the care was a Medicare-covered service or not. The logic was that patients had a right to contract privately for medical care services, and any restrictions regarding excess fees did not apply if Medicare was not billed.

The legislation that created Medicare Part C did include a provision for private contracting between doctors and patients. However, a hitch—known as Section 4507—was attached to the bill with virtually no publicity or debate. Section 4507 prohibits Medicare patients from going outside Medicare for Medicare-covered services and paying for them out of pocket *unless the doctor who provides the services forswears any Medicare program involvement for at least 2 years.* Of course, Medicare patients are free to obtain *noncovered* services on their own if they choose to pay for the service themselves.

Section 4507 is supposed to prevent doctors from treating both Medicare patients and Medicare-eligible private patients at the same time. The fear, held by those opposed to patients being able to contract privately for Medicare-covered services, is that it would lead to a two-tier system with private patients getting more and better medical care for Medicare covered services than their Medicare-pay counterparts. It was also asserted that under such private arrangements there would be "no limit" to what a physician might charge a patient.

From an economic perspective, this argument reveals a profound ignorance of market processes. Rather than a two-tier system, what is more likely to develop is a no-tier system. For instance, a specialist who has opted out of Medicare because he or she contracts privately with Medicare-eligible patients may be willing but unable under Section 4507 to take on a Medicare-pay patient. In addition, as we have observed in relation to many other transactions: "for every seller there must be a buyer." The market for medical services is no exception, and in voluntary transactions, the price of *anything* has a limit, namely, what the buyer will pay. If market transactions actually revealed that the prices physicians were able to get for their services were "exorbitantly high," the forces of supply and demand soon would provide more doctors seeking those prices, and fees would collapse. If allowed to develop unfettered, a genuinely private medical services market almost surely would, all else equal, see a slower rate of increase in medical costs.

What Should You Do?

Currently, America's senior citizens have limited experience with Medicare Advantage options other than HMOs. Very often it is the newest products to reach the health care market that carry the highest costs to consumers (as with, say, long-term care policies when they first were introduced) partly because providers lack claims and loss experience. On the other hand, sometimes "getting in on the ground floor" is the best way to save money. For the health care consumer, this situation may further complicate the task of finding the lowest-cost protection against the expense of illness and incapacity.

In these circumstances, seniors should remain as flexible as possible. The regional PPOs authorized by the 2003 Medicare legislation may offer an attractive alternative for many Medicare beneficiaries who appreciate the benefits of managed care, but want more than a local network of providers. The pros and cons will become clearer after the PPO regions are determined by the Secretary of Health and Human Services in 2004. But whatever options eventually reach the market, the underlying financial considerations discussed in the previous chapters will not change: *cover the major risks first*, which means acquiring the most comprehensive tail-end coverage available, whoever the provider may be.

VI.

ALTERNATIVES TO HEALTH INSURANCE POLICIES

FOR a number of years, many health-related insurance policies have aimed at the Medicare market. This is understandable. For the past 50 years, the retired have had the most reliable incomes of any segment of the population. Although smaller in relation to their working-years' incomes, the more-or-less guaranteed aspect of retirement income, combined with the health consequences of aging, generated a great deal of market interest within the insurance industry.

One result of this interest has been the proliferation of limited-coverage health policies. These are *not* to be confused with medigap supplemental insurance policies, which are discussed in the next chapter. Rather, these policies provide much narrower coverage. They have relatively low premiums and are affordable to most retired persons. However, they cover only a small portion of the potential health risk of the elderly. They cover isolated diseases or situations, and their sales approach generally exploits the understandable fears of most of us. **Limited-coverage policies are not the bargains they appear to be and are no substitute for comprehensive insurance.**

In general, any policy that limits coverage to a particular set of conditions violates the health insurance principle, which is to reduce potential risk regardless of the circumstances of illness. All states allow the sale of limited policies in one form or another. But Federal law prohibits their sale as "supplemental health insurance." Limited policies such as accident, "dread disease" or cancer, and daily indemnity insurance leave wide gaps in coverage and thus in financial risk. Their traditional popularity testifies powerfully to the persistence of the myths surrounding elderly health risks. For the most part, these policies create only the illusion of greater protection.

Accident Insurance

Accident insurance is *not* health insurance. These policies pay hospital and medical costs only if you have been injured as a result of accident. They frequently impose limits on benefits that are far below actual costs of rehabilitation.

Accident indemnity policies, which promise to pay a specified amount for the loss of one or both eyes, arms, or legs in an accident, are so narrowly written that they apply only in an infinitesimally small set of circumstances. Amputees who have had their limbs removed for clinical reasons, for example, are not protected by such policies. *Accident insurance is a waste of money.*

"Dread Disease" and Cancer Policies

These policies, which usually are solicited either through the mail, in newspapers and magazines, or by salesmen working on commission, are notoriously poor values. They appeal to unrealistic fears, cover only very specific conditions, and cannot substitute for comprehensive insurance. Consequently, some states have prohibited their sale.

Even if you contract an insured disease, you will not likely be hospitalized long enough to receive the benefits that would justify the premiums on these policies. Moreover, special disease policies normally do not provide protection against many types of costs incurred as a result of the disease, such as home care, transportation, and rehabilitation.

Most cancer policies contain one or more of the following limiting conditions:

- Some pay only if you are hospitalized. Today, most cancer care, such as radiation treatment and chemotherapy, is provided on an outpatient basis. The average hospital stay for cancer patients is only about seven days.

- No policy will provide protection against cancer diagnosed before you applied for the policy.

- Most cancer insurance does not cover related illnesses, such as infection, diabetes, or pneumonia.

- These policies often require waiting periods of anywhere from 30 days to several months before coverage becomes effective. Many stop paying benefits after a fixed period of 24 or 36 months.

- Although a number of these policies increase coverage after 90 consecutive days in the hospital, this feature is nearly worthless since 99 percent of all cancer patients spend fewer than 60 days in the hospital.

Cancer policies have traditionally posted the lowest loss ratios (the percentage of premiums that are returned to policyholders as benefits)—sometimes only 20 percent—of all forms of health insurance. As with accident indemnity policies, *special disease insurance is a waste of money.*

Hospital Indemnity Policies

Hospital indemnity policies that promise to pay you a fixed amount for each day you spend in the hospital have been widely advertised on television. Actors hired for their high "trust quotients" counsel elderly viewers in soothing yet urgent tones to subscribe to their particular plan, which is often made to sound exclusive. In fact, indemnity policies that usually promise to pay between $50 and $100 a day are not health insurance. Although they may be useful in some circumstances, as discussed below, *the average benefit return does not justify the premium cost of this kind of policy.*

Indemnity policies may have value under some conditions. Advertisements describe them as supplemental income plans; the law prohibits them from being advertised as otherwise. If you already have supplemental insurance, an indemnity policy may be attractive as a source of income in the event of extended hospitalization. This type of benefit can help to defray associated expenses, such as transportation and home maintenance, that may not otherwise be covered by health insurance.

Many people buy indemnity policies hoping they will "make money" if they get sick. Purchased this way, an indemnity policy is merely a gamble similar to buying a lottery ticket. If your potential risk does not justify the policy—either because it is too high or too low—you are throwing your money away.

Whether or not an indemnity policy is worthwhile depends on two separate considerations. First, to what extent will hospitalization place you at financial risk for non-medical reasons? Second, to what extent will the policy reduce this financial risk?

Everyone incurs some non-medical expense as a result of hospital confinement. If nothing else, the lawn has to be mowed and household chores have to be done. The important question is: Can these

57

routine expenses be handled out of pocket, or does your situation involve financial risk that merits the purchase of separate income insurance? For example, would you have to hire full-time help to maintain your residence while you were in the hospital? Would you suffer a loss of essential income? Would others be deprived of your needed services because of your absence (if, say, your spouse or another household member relies on you for daily care)? Do you conduct a business that would require you to employ someone if you were in the hospital? In short, the extent of your non-medical risk determines if you should consider an indemnity policy. This assumes that you can afford its premium costs over and above the price of supplemental health insurance. *You should not sacrifice supplemental health insurance coverage in order to pay premiums on a hospital indemnity policy.*

Employer-Sponsored Health Insurance

Many employers offer health insurance. These group employee plans often give the best value available in health insurance to employees, and many—though not all—are convertible to Medicare supplemental plans after retirement. If your employer offers a health insurance plan, you should contact the personnel or benefits office to find out what kind of protection is available to you after retirement. *As a rule, employer-sponsored health insurance offers a far better value than individual policies*, but not always. You must compare it with other forms of health coverage, such as the Medicare HMOs that are discussed in Chapter V.

Employers have been cutting back on health benefits for retirees for some years, and they are expected to continue to do so. Large businesses typically have offered the most generous benefits, and they now pay over half of total retiree medical expenses. But the most generous plans would appear to be especially vulnerable to cutbacks as employers seek to slow the rapid growth of health-care costs. Although many changes will likely be borne by current employees and especially new hires, retirees should be prepared for possible changes (such as reduced coverage or higher premiums and copayments) or even termination of their employer-sponsored health insurance. Unlike pension benefits, retiree health benefits usually are *not* guaranteed.

If you lose your employer-sponsored retiree coverage, Federal

58

law gives you the right to buy Medicare supplemental insurance plans A, B, C, or F (described fully in Chapter VII) within 63 days of the date you lose your group coverage. In practice, your options may be more limited than this suggests, because not all policies are offered in every state. In any event, the insurance company cannot deny you a policy if it is available, place conditions on the policy such as a waiting period, apply a pre-existing condition exclusion, or discriminate in the price of the policy based on your health status. Make sure you keep a copy of your employer-plan's termination letter. Also, check your own state's regulations regarding such terminations, because some states provide more medigap protection than Federal law.

A small percentage of employers offer their employees health plans that are totally independent of the insurance industry. Termed "self-insurance," the employer assumes some or all of the risk of the health plan. Instead of paying premiums to an insurance company, the employer pays claims from its own funds and contracts independently with physicians and hospitals to provide health care to its employees. In a few instances, such as the Kaiser complex in California, employers have constructed their own hospital facilities. Self-funding gives employees greater flexibility and control of their health benefits plan.

From the retired employee's perspective, the health care provided by self-insured employers probably differs little from what is offered through conventional employer-sponsored insurance plans. But as rising health-care costs become more onerous for all employers, these self-insured plans are subject to the same restrictions in coverage and increases in the retiree's share of costs as any other employer-sponsored plan.

VII.

MEDICARE SUPPLEMENTAL INSURANCE

SINCE 1992, any insurer offering Medicare supplemental insurance has been required to restrict policy offerings to ten "approved" policies labeled A through J as stipulated by Federal and subsequent state regulations. In 1997, Congress allowed insurers to also offer a "high-deductible" option for plans F and J. This does not mean that insurance companies are prohibited from selling other types of policies. But they may not be called "Medicare supplemental insurance."

You do not need to buy a Medicare supplemental policy if you are in a Medicare managed-care plan (such as an HMO) or if you are covered by Medicaid. Generally, in such cases, it is not legal for anyone to sell you one.

In this chapter we describe the major provisions of each of these ten policies. With the important exceptions noted below, in states that have approved the National Association of Insurance Commissioners (NAIC) model regulation, any Medicare supplemental insurance policy offered for sale must adhere strictly to those provisions. The intent of the framers of these model standards was to simplify the medigap insurance decisions of consumers by requiring that insurers offer policies that are strictly comparable, thus permitting accurate "price shopping."

However, certain loopholes may permit insurers to tinker with the NAIC standardized policies. According to the NAIC regulation, "The issuer of a Medicare supplement policy may, with the prior approval of the [State] commissioner [of insurance], offer new or innovative benefits in addition to the benefits provided in a policy that otherwise complies with the applicable standards." And according to the Omnibus Budget Reconciliation Act of 1990, issuers of Medicare supplement policies are not prohibited from offering discounts to policyholders "for the purchase of items or services not covered under its Medicare supplement policies (for example: discounts on hearing aids or eyeglasses)." In short, the insurers may simply find new ways to make their medigap policies unique—which would largely defeat the intent of the "simplified" NAIC regulations.

In addition, different types of policies are sold in Massachusetts, Minnesota, and Wisconsin because these states already required standardized medigap policies prior to 1992. If you reside in one of these states, contact your State Insurance Department for more information. See Chapter VIII for contact information.

The Ten NAIC-Approved
Medicare Supplemental Insurance Plans

However, the NAIC regulation is very specific about the benefits that the ten approved policies *must* contain. Any insurer who wants to sell Medicare supplemental insurance in a state must offer a basic policy (Policy A) that contains only the "core" benefits that are common to all approved policies. Insurers who offer the core policy may or may not offer any or all of the other approved policies that contain additional benefits. However, no policy may duplicate coverage that is provided by either Medicare Part A or Part B. The terms of coverage provided by the ten Medicare supplemental insurance policies approved in the NAIC model regulation are summarized in Table 2 on page 64. The specific provisions of each of the policies are as follows. (A review of Medicare Part A and B coverage, explained in Chapter II, may be helpful at this point.)

Plan A (core policy) provides: The Medicare copayment (in 2004) of $219 per day for hospital stays for days 61–90 and $438 per day for days 91–150; up to 365 days of hospital expenses during your lifetime once Medicare Part A hospital benefits are used up; the Medicare co-payment (generally 20 percent of doctors' services) under Medicare Part B after you have met the $100 deductible; and the first three pints of blood each year

Plan A thus provides basic coverage for the hospitalization costs of catastrophic illness up to a year after Medicare benefits cease and for medical costs for all Medicare-approved charges. All ten Medicare Supplemental insurance policies must contain these core benefits.

In addition, as outlined in the table on page 66, **Plans B-J** must cover the Part A hospital deductible—$876 in 2004. Following that, **Plans C-J**, must cover the copayment for skilled nursing-home care for days 21-100 ($109.50 a day in 2004) and medically necessary emergency care in a foreign country (80 percent of the cost during the first 60 days of each trip after $250 deductible, $50,000 lifetime limit). Plans C-J also provide an assortment of additional benefits, depending on the plan, as described below.

Plan C includes the Part B Medical Insurance deductible ($100 per year).

Plan D includes at-home recovery ($40 per visit to a maximum of $1,600 per year; doctor certification required).

Plan E includes preventive screening and care.

Plan F includes 100 percent of excess charges under Part B Medical Insurance (*i.e.*, the difference between your doctor's charge and Medicare's approved charge if your doctor does not accept assignment).

Plan F also has an option called the High-Deductible Plan F, which pays the same benefits as regular Plan F after you pay a deductible each year ($1,690 in 2004). This deductible increases each year by the percentage increase in the Consumer Price Index for all urban consumers (CPI-U) for the 12-month period ending with August of the preceding year.

Plan G includes at-home recovery care and 80 percent of excess charges under Part B Medical Insurance.

Plan H includes coverage of 50 percent of the cost of outpatient prescription drugs after a $250 deductible, up to a maximum benefit of $1,250.

Plan I includes at-home recovery care, 100 percent of excess charges under Part B Medical Insurance, and 50 percent of the cost of outpatient prescription drugs after a $250 deductible, up to a maximum benefit of $1,250.

Plan J includes at-home recovery care, 100 percent of excess charges under Part B Medical Insurance, preventive screening and care, and 50 percent of the cost of outpatient prescription drugs after a $250 deductible, up to a maximum benefit of $3,000.

Plan J also has a high-deductible option that pays the same benefits as regular Plan J after you pay a deductible of $1,690 in 2004. The deductible increases each year by the percentage increase in the Consumer Price Index for all urban consumers (CPI-U) for the 12-

Table 2
NAIC MEDICARE SUPPLEMENT PLAN STANDARDS

Benefit	A	B	C	D	E	F²	G	H	I	J²
Core¹	✓	✓	✓	✓	✓	✓	✓	✓	✓	✓
Part A (hospital) deductible		✓	✓	✓	✓	✓	✓	✓	✓	✓
Skilled nursing facility			✓	✓	✓	✓	✓	✓	✓	✓
Foreign emergency care			✓	✓	✓	✓	✓	✓	✓	✓
Part B (physician) deductible			✓			✓				✓
Part B (physician) excess charges						100%	80%		100%	100%
At-home recovery care				✓			✓		✓	✓
Prescription drugs								Basic³	Basic³	Ext'd³
Preventive screening					✓					✓
Average Annual Premium⁴	$1,057	1,303	1,579	1,338	1,365	1,627	1,456	2,360	2,423	2,734
Distribution of Sales⁵	13.2%	6.8	19.3	6.8	3.2	36.8	5.1	1.0	2.4	3.7

[1] Core benefits include: Part A (hospital) coinsurance plus a lifetime maximum benefit for an additional 365 days; Part B (physician) coinsurance, subject to the Part B deductible; and the first three (3) pints of blood each year. [2] Plans F and J also have a high deductible option ($1,690 in 2004). [3] Basic coverage: After you pay $250 per year deductible, the plan pays 50% of prescription drug costs up to a maximum of $1,250 per year ($3,000 per year for extended coverage). [4] Weiss Ratings, 2003. [5] NAIC, 2002, figures for 2001.

month period ending with August of the preceding year.

Only plans H, I, and J provide prescription drug coverage. The extra premium for this limited coverage may be substantial. In any event, current drug coverage will be dropped from standard medigap policies when the new Medicare prescription drug benefit becomes available in 2006. And beginning in May 2004, Medicare beneficiaries will have the option of buying a Medicare drug discount card to help with their drug costs. Given these upcoming changes, it is questionable whether it is still worth buying a medigap policy primarily for its prescription drug coverage.

Under the new Medicare law, insurance policies that cover *only* prescription drugs will become available in less than two years. Depending on what you expect your drug costs to be from now until 2006, the drug coverage that plans H, I, and J offer may or may not be worth the extra premiums. However, this coverage is not the only thing that distinguishes plans H, I, and J from other medigap plans, as can be seen in the table on page 64. Their other benefits may still make them worth considering, depending on their premiums and on your particular needs.

Few insurance companies offer all ten standard medigap plans. They usually do not find it profitable to offer every type of plan in every area of the country. In theory you have ten plans from which to choose, but in practice your choices may be much more limited.

Medicare SELECT

Medicare SELECT was introduced on a trial basis in 15 states in 1994, expanded to all 50 states in 1995, and made permanent in 1998. If you buy a Medicare SELECT policy, you are buying one of the ten standardized medigap plans A through J. With a Medicare SELECT policy, you must use a specific network of hospitals and, in some cases, doctors within that network, to get full insurance benefits (except in an emergency). For this reason, Medicare SELECT premiums are typically lower than comparable medigap policies that do not have this selected-provider feature. Relatively few of these policies have been sold and they are not available in all states. For more information call your state insurance department (see Chapter VIII).

If you have a Medicare SELECT policy and you move out of the plan's service area, you will have to change your insurance coverage. You have the right to buy medigap plans A, B, C, or F that are sold in the state to which you move.

How Much Does Medigap Insurance Cost?

Costs vary widely from plan to plan, from insurance company to insurance company, and from state to state. Hence, it is in your financial interest to shop around. The table on page 64 shows the average annual premium for each of the various standardized plans as of 2003, according to Weiss Ratings. Table 3 below shows the highest and lowest premium rates for each type of plan. According to Weiss Ratings, the annual premium for Plan F, the most popular plan, ranges from a minimum of $617 to a maximum of $4,419, and the average premium is $1,627. Overall, premiums range from a minimum of $352 for Plan A to a maximum of $9,769 for Plan H. Plans H, I, and J – the only ones that cover prescription drugs – cost much more than the other standardized plans.

When comparing premiums, you should try to estimate your likely costs over a five or ten period: both what you will pay when you first buy the policy and what it will cost in the future. Both figures depend on the method used by insurers to price the policy. If a policy is "community rated," all policy holders, regardless of age, pay the same premium. Companies are required to sell community-rated policies in Connecticut, Maine, Massachusetts, Minnesota, New York, and Washington. If a policy is "issue-age rated," the premium will depend on the age of the beneficiary at the time the policy is pur-

Table 3
Premium Rates for Medigap Insurance

Plan	Minimum	Maximum	Average
A	$352	$2,851	$1,057
B	444	3,158	1,303
C	577	4,013	1,579
D	480	3,373	1,338
E	768	4,762	1,365
F	617	4,419	1,627
G	773	3,807	1,456
H	1,324	9,769	2,360
I	1,332	5,730	2,423
J	1,570	6,659	2,734

Based on a national survey of 103 insurance companies. Source: Weiss Ratings, 2003.

chased. Florida and Georgia require companies to sell this type of policy.

Most medigap policies today, however, are "attained-age rated." With attained-age policies, premiums rise as you get older. For example, while the initial premium for an attained-age policy is generally lower than that of either a community-rated or issue-age rated policy, just the opposite situation usually develops as the beneficiary ages; an attained-age policy with an attractive premium at age 65 may not turn out to be the same bargain when you reach age 70 or 75.

Depending on the insurance company, your gender, smoking habits, and marital status may also affect your premiums. And, of course, none of the aforementioned pricing methods takes into account the unpredictable but always upward pressure of both price inflation and capricious government regulation.

The Relative Value of Plan Options

What you pay for a medigap policy largely depends on how much coverage you want—the more the coverage, the more the cost. You should not, however, purchase the most comprehensive policy just because you can afford the premiums—the plan may not be worth the additional premiums you would pay for it.

There are five benefits you need to consider when comparing Plans C through J, as shown in the table on page 64: the Part B deductible; Part B charges that exceed what Medicare approves; at-home recovery care; prescription drugs; and preventive screening. However, the Part B deductible ($100) and preventive screening benefits ($120) are minor expenses and so are less important than the other remaining options—Part B excess charges, at-home recovery, and prescription drugs.

At-home recovery benefits are quite limited, paying no more than $40 per visit and $1,600 per year. In order to receive this benefit, you must be receiving Medicare-covered home health services already. Medicare coverage may be ample for the same services that the at-home recovery benefit would cover. Unless you are considering the costly prescription drug benefit (see below), in which case at-home recovery would likely be a minor consideration, Plans D and G are your only choices for at-home recovery coverage.

If the Part B excess-charge benefit (potentially much greater than the at-home recovery benefit) is important to you, then you cannot choose a plan that will pay 100 percent of those charges if you also want at-home recovery coverage; instead, you will be limited to Plan G, which provides only 80 percent coverage of Part B excess charges. Though Part B excess charges are now somewhat less important than they were because of federal and state limitations on balance billing, they can still be formidable. For instance, $115,000 worth of physician bills that were 15 percent above Medicare's allowed charge would leave you with a liability of $15,000. And, unlike the at-home recovery coverage, Part B excess-charge benefits are not capped.

Your decision on coverage may, therefore, be simplified, particularly if you have some idea of your particular risks relating to Part B excess charges and prescription drugs, since these are the two benefits that could make the largest difference in your costs, assuming you are choosing a policy from Plan C through Plan J. If you think Part B excess charges are likely to be important, Plans F, I, or J give maximum benefits; Plan G provides the 80 percent benefit.

If you think prescription drugs are likely to be important between now and 2006 (when the new Medicare drug benefit will become available), Plans H and I give basic coverage; Plan J gives extended coverage. However, the prescription drug benefit makes these plans expensive. According to Weiss Ratings, the premiums for all three medigap plans with prescription-drug coverage (Plans H, I, and J) averaged more than $2,500. Because of the deductible ($250) and 50 percent coinsurance, you would have to spend at least $2,750 a year for drugs to get the full $1,250 benefit for Plans H and I. For Plan J, you must spend $6,250 a year on prescription drugs to get the full $3,000 benefit.

Is drug coverage worth it to you? To answer the question, you must estimate your expected annual prescription costs between now and 2006. When the new Medicare prescription drug benefit is introduced in 2006, the drug coverage currently offered in these plans H, I, and J will no longer be offered to new buyers. Instead, you will have the right to buy a separate prescription drug insurance policy. Beginning in May 2004 you will also have the right to buy a Medicare drug discount card that, according to Medicare, will provide savings of 10 to 25 percent off the retail price of drugs.

If you currently own a medigap policy with drug coverage, or you purchase one between now and 2006, you will be allowed to keep it after the new Medicare drug benefit becomes available, but the coverage may change. If you eventually decide to buy one of the new prescription drug insurance policies that will become available in 2006, any drug coverage on your old medigap policy will be dropped and the premium reduced to reflect this.

Plans F and C are the most widely held plans, accounting for over half of all medigap policies purchased. They are identical except that Plan F covers Part B excess charges. Neither plan covers at-home recovery expenses or prescription drugs.

Beware the "Hard Sell"

Whenever major changes occur in a program such as Medicare, opportunities are created for the insurance companies to exploit a newly created market. Today, the "Medicare roller coaster" has created just such an opportunity and, not surprisingly, the sales forces of most health insurers have marshaled their considerable talents to convince Medicare subscribers that they need their company's policy. As in all such situations, exaggeration of risks and benefits sometimes plays a part in the sales presentation. We review below a number of tactics—and potential sales abuses—to which consumers should be alert.

"Lead cards." Reportedly, Medicare subscribers in many states are being mailed what are called "lead cards" in order to identify potential supplemental insurance buyers. Usually, these mailings come in official-looking envelopes with an official-sounding name that conveys the impression the sender is connected with a Government agency. The enclosed letter may warn of supposed great risks faced by the elderly as a result of changes in Medicare and usually offers the addressee important information if the enclosed form is filled out (stating name, address, age, Social Security number, and the like) and returned to the sender. Often, the subject of insurance is not mentioned in the lead card, but that is the purpose of the mailing.

In fact, the names and addresses that are returned on the cards to the marketing firm are then sold to insurance companies or their agents as "hot prospects" for Medicare supplemental insurance or "alternative" insurance policies. Some states, such as California, have clamped down on these practices. If you receive such a mailing, you should be aware that if you return the card, in all likelihood your name will be sold to an insurer who then will try to sell you a policy.

Appeals to urgency. Insurance salespersons may stress that you must "act now" to get the most coverage from a particular insurance policy. However, once a policy prospectus has been developed, the terms of coverage for that policy will not change no matter how long a buyer waits to purchase it. High-pressure sales techniques that stress the urgency of acquiring a particular policy simply are designed to get you to purchase as soon as possible.

In some situations, however, it may make sense to buy a policy sooner rather than later. For example, if you have decided that a policy provides adequate coverage at a reasonable cost, and if premium costs will increase if, say, you become a year older (for insurance purposes) at an imminent birth date, it will save you money to sign the insurance contract before that time.

Duplicate coverage. The NAIC Model Standards prevent supplemental policies from duplicating Medicare benefits, but they do not address the sale of policies that may replicate *other* supplemental policies. Although it violates most states' fair sales practices legislation, insurance sales personnel may try to find a way around the rules and sell you what amounts to duplicate coverage. For example, the salesperson may not inquire if you already own a Medicare supplemental policy, and if challenged later be able to say that he or she was unaware that the policy offered replicated existing coverage. Or the sales pitch may emphasize that the offered policy provides additional coverage beyond the supplemental policy you own and that both are needed to provide "comprehensive protection." Do not be deceived by such appeals. You should look for the best supplemental policy for your circumstances and buy that policy and only that policy.

"Mining for gold." Beware of salespeople who immediately try to find out how much you are worth. They may want to know how large a policy they can sell, not what may be the best buy for you. Do not offer information about your personal finances. After all alternatives have been explored and you have had a chance to compare a number of different policies at your leisure and out of the watchful eye of the salesperson, you may want to review how much insurance you can afford with a *disinterested* third party (your financial adviser or banker, for example). But opening your financial account books to the insurance salesperson may invite sales abuses.

Evaluating the Insurers

Industry specialists generally agree about what the future of health care insurance holds: higher premiums, rate increases, restructured benefit offerings, additional "out-of-pocket" expenses, continued growth in the size of the uninsured population, more mergers and acquisitions, and more failures by health care companies. Furthermore, a host of regulatory and performance issues will affect various products and markets.

The combination of sharply rising health care costs, Government regulation, actuarial imprecision, and managerial confusion has resulted in substantial underwriting losses for some insurers in the past decade or so. (Underwriting losses occur when companies pay out more in benefits and operating expenses than they take in as premium income.) One might well question how insurance companies can continue in business after taking losses. All insurance companies have two sources of income—premiums and investments. For most of the last decade, premium income was inadequate to cover benefit expenditures. But until a few years ago, investment income more than made up for premium losses. More recently, however, investment gains have not been sufficient to offset underwriting losses.

Heavy reliance on unstable investment returns has made insurers especially vulnerable to a situation where health care costs and benefit payments have continued to increase while offsetting yields on investments have become harder to achieve. In short, many insurance companies now find themselves in a classic financial squeeze, a situation that has led some industry analysts to speculate that "shakeouts" may occur—that is, weaker companies will be forced out of business or merged with healthier ones.

You do have some protection in case the industry squeeze affects your policy. If your medigap coverage ceases because of the bankruptcy or insolvency of your insurer, Federal law gives you the right to buy either medigap plan A, B, C, or F within 63 days of the date you lose your coverage, provided the medigap plan is offered in your state. The insurance company cannot deny you the policy, place conditions on the policy such as a waiting period, apply a pre-existing condition exclusion, or discriminate in the price of the policy based on your health status. Make sure you keep a copy of your plan's termination letter. (Some states provide more medigap protection than Federal law.)

These guarantees may be of small comfort to you if your previous medigap policy was in a plan other than Plan A, B, C, or F and you still desire the benefits of that plan. Furthermore, if your new policy is not community-rated, you may face a premium penalty.

Therefore, *before* buying any policy you should take care to ascertain that it is offered by a healthy insurer—and that it is likely to return good value. With respect to insurer health, we recommend that policies be purchased only from companies that are highly rated by two major ratings agencies, A.M. Best and Weiss Ratings. Their ratings represent an opinion based on a comprehensive evaluation of each company's financial strength, operating performance, and market profile. These ratings are described in Chapter VIII.

Another useful measure of both the financial health of a company and the value that it returns to policyholders is the so-called loss ratio, which represents the percentage of premiums that are returned to policyholders as benefits. Many state departments of insurance (see listing in Chapter VIII) have prepared brief guides to supplemental health insurance for Medicare subscribers. And a number of these advise supplemental insurance buyers to use insurance companies' loss ratios as a way to compare the relative value of policies. Extraordinarily low loss ratios of between 20 and 40 percent, for example, are a sign that a policy is not returning value to policyholders. Federal law stipulates that a cumulative 65 percent loss ratio for individual policies (75 percent for group policies) must be met over the life of a policy, which is assumed to be 15 years. Insurers are required to pay refunds or provide credits to policyholders when policies fail to meet loss ratio standards.

Traditionally, insurance actuaries aim for underwriting loss ratios in the range of 70 to 75 percent. Losses in this range allow a company to retain an attractive marketing stance, yet still permit the company to turn an acceptable underwriting profit. Losses much over 75 percent, however, may be risky to the company—and here a difference of a few percentage points can make the difference between profit and loss, and, eventually, between solvency and insolvency. In 1999, according to the Government Accounting Office, the 15 largest sellers of medigap policies had loss ratios ranging from 64 to 88 percent.

In short, be sure to check out the financial health as well as the benefits and premium costs of any insurer whose policy you are considering. Even the best coverage at a low price will be useless if the company cannot pay claims promptly (or at all).

VIII.
SHOPPING FOR
A MEDICARE SUPPLEMENTAL POLICY

INSURANCE agents are trained to emphasize the advantages of their company's policies and the drawbacks of their competitors' products. Insurance salespeople hope to convince you that their policy represents the best value by "comparing" it with other policies. Do not be deceived. These sales-oriented comparisons often are designed to make one policy look much better than all the rest and are unreliable. In all likelihood, few, if any, companies will offer all ten medigap plans—and they will, no doubt, develop sales presentations that emphasize the benefits only of the plans they do offer.

Ultimately, it is up to you to find the best value through independent inquiry. Do not rely on salespeople and do not rely on friends who claim to have found a "great deal." Friends may be well-meaning, but they also may not have all the facts relevant to your situation.

Every State Is Different

Premium costs from company to company and from state to state vary widely. Even within some states, prices on the same policy are different. In fact, in the larger metropolitan areas of the Northeast and the Midwest, your premium cost may depend on the side of town in which you reside. In short, a policy that may represent the best value in one state or locality will not necessarily be the best value in another state or locality. You cannot rely on the advice of friends who reside outside your area.

A number of state insurance departments or related state agencies have consumer affairs divisions that provide information free to prospective medigap insurance buyers. As a first step in shopping for a Medicare supplemental policy, contact your state agency as shown in the directory in this chapter. Request a list of all Medicare supplemental insurance providers currently offering policies in your locality. Make certain you get current addresses and telephone numbers. Also, ask for any related literature. A number of states have prepared guides to supplemental insurance, and most contain pertinent information regarding the peculiarities of such insurance in

75

NATIONAL DIRECTORY
OF STATE INSURANCE DEPARTMENTS

Write or telephone the State Insurance Department at the following locations:

Alabama, Montgomery 36130 www.aldoi.org 334-269-3550
Alaska, Juneau 99811-3422 www.dced.state.ak.us/insurance 907-465-2515
Arizona, Phoenix 85018 www.state.az.us/id/ 602-912-8400
Arkansas, Little Rock 72201 www.state.ar.us/insurance/ 501-371-2600
California, Sacramento 95814 www.aging.ca.gov 916-492-3500

Colorado, Denver 80202 www.dora.state.co.us.insurance 303-894-7499
Connecticut, Hartford 06142-0816 www.state.ct.us/cid/ 860-297-3800
Delaware, Dover 19904 www.state.de.us/inscom/eldindex.htm . 302-739-4251
D.C., Washington 20004 disr.washingtondc.gov.insurance 202-727-8000
Florida, Tallahassee 32399-0300 www.doi.state.fl.us/ 850-413-2806

Georgia, Atlanta 30334 www.inscomm.state.ga.us/ 404-656-2056
Hawaii, Honolulu 96813 www.state.hi.us/dcca/ins/ 808-586-2790
Idaho, Boise 83720-0043 www.doi.state.id.us/ 208-334-4250
Illinois, Springfield 62767 www.state.il.us/ins/ 217-782-4515
Indiana, Indianapolis 46204-2787 www.ai.org/idoi/ 317-232-2385

Iowa, Des Moines 50319 www.shiip.state.ia.us/ 515-281-5705
Kansas, Topeka 66612-1678 www.ksinsurance.org/ 785-296-3071
Kentucky, Frankfort 40602 www.doi.state.ky.us/ 502-564-6027
Louisiana, Baton Rouge 70804-9214 www.ldi.state.la.us/ 225-342-5423
Maine, Augusta 04333 www.state.me.us/ 207-624-8475

Maryland, Baltimore 21202-2272 www.mdinsurance.state.md.us/ 410-468-2000
Massachusetts, Boston 02216 www.state.ma.us/consumer/ 617-973-8787
Michigan, Lansing 48917-4850 www.mymmap.org 517-373-0220
Minnesota, St. Paul 55101 www.commerce.state.mn.us/ 651-296-6025
Mississippi, Jackson 39201 www.doi.state.ms.us/ 601-359-3569

Missouri, Jefferson City 65102-1527 wwwdss.state.mo.us/. 573-751-4126
Montana, Helena 59601www.dphhs.state.mt.us/sltc/index/htm .. 406-444-2040
Nebraska, Lincoln 68505-3639 www.nol.org/home/NDOI/. 402-471-2201
Nevada, Carson City 89701 www.dio.state.nv.us/ 775-687-4270
New Hampshire, Concord 03301-7317www.nhhelpline.org/hiceas/index.cfm 603-271-2261

New Jersey, Trenton 08625-0325 www.state.nj.us/dobi/ 609-292-5360
New Mexico, Santa Fe 87504 www.mnaging.state.nm.us/ 505-827-4601
New York, Albany 12257 www.ins.state.ny.us/caremain.htm 518-474-4567
North Carolina, Raleigh 27611www.ncdoi.com/ 919-733-3058
North Dakota, Bismarck 58505-0320 www.state.nd.us/ndins/ 701-328-2440

Ohio, Columbus 43215 www.ohioinsurance.gov	614-644-2658
Oklahoma, Oklahoma City 73152-3408 www.oid.state.ok.us/	405-522-4969
Oregon, Salem 97301-3883 www.cbs.state.or.us/	503-947-7980
Pennsylvania, Harrisburg 17120 www.ins.state.pa.us/..............	717-863-0442
Rhode Island, Providence 02903 www.dbr.state.ri.us/	401-222-5466
South Carolina, Columbia 29223 www.doi.state.sc.us/	803-737-6212
South Dakota, Pierre 57501 www.state.sd.us/insurance	605-773-4104
Tennessee, Nashville 37243 www.state.tn.us/commerce	615-741-6007
Texas, Austin 78701-9104 www.tdi.state.tx.us	512-463-6464
Utah, Salt Lake City 84114-1010 www.insurance.utah.gov	801-538-3800
Vermont, Montpelier 05620-3101 www.bishca.state.vt.us	802-828-3301
Virginia, Richmond 23219 www.state.va.us/scc	804-371-9694
Washington, Olympia 98504-0255 www.insurance.wa.gov ...	360-725-7100
West Virginia, Charleston 25305-0540 www.state.wv.us/insurance	304-558-3354
Wisconsin, Madison 53702 www.oci.wi.gov	608-267-1233
Wyoming, Cheyenne 82002 www.insurance.state.wy.us/	307-777-7401

their states.

You may also obtain a list of medigap providers in your area by calling 1-800-MEDICARE (1-800-633-4227) or by visiting the Medicare website at www.medicare.gov and using the "Medicare Personal Plan Finder." This interactive section helps you figure out what type of insurance you need, lists the available policies, and also links you to the appropriate insurance company websites.

When you have obtained a list of Medicare supplemental insurance providers for your area, contact each one. Request full policy details, including coverage, exclusions or restrictions, waiting periods, renewability, and premium rates. If any policy does not meet the NAIC Model Standards or the additional requirements of your state, contact the State Insurance Department and report the discrepancy.

Evaluating Insurance Companies

To determine the status of each company for which you have a policy prospectus, consult the major ratings agencies that evaluate the strength of insurance companies. Each has its own method of evaluation.

A.M. Best is the oldest insurance evaluator. The company publishes monthly and annual reports on a variety of issues concerning the insurance industry. Its flagship publication is *Best's Insurance Reports: Life and Health*. Even fewer insurance buyers know about *Best's* than about their state insurance department, but it is an equally useful resource. The reference librarian in your local library will direct you to *Best's Reports*. You can also get Best's ratings online for free at www.ambest.com.

For many individuals, the online Best's rating will be sufficient. If you want more detailed information, however, consult *Best's Reports* for the most recent year available. This will be a large, heavy, red bound volume that resembles an encyclopedia in looks and contains nearly as much information. (Some libraries also carry it in electronic form.) *Best's Reports* lists virtually all insurance companies currently writing policies in the United States.

A.M. Best rates each company on a letter grade: A++ (superior), A+, A, or A- (excellent), B++ or B+ (good), B or B- (adequate), C++ or C+ (below average), C, C-, D (weak), and E or F (nonviable). Any company with a B rating or lower is being "damned with faint praise." As a general rule, it is advisable to insure only with those companies rated A or higher.

Financial-strength ratings are also available from Weiss Ratings, Inc. This company uses an especially conservative approach and rates only a few companies as superior. It rates companies on a letter scale ranging from A+ (strongest) to F (weakest). Weiss rates the financial status of over 1,700 health-insurance companies, 700 HMOs, and all of the Blue Cross Blue Shield plans. A rating for one company costs $19.00 over the phone (a representative will give you a full description of what the rating means) or $15.99 for a one-page report purchased online. For more information, call (800) 289-9222 or go to the Weiss website, www.weissratings.com.

Weiss also publishes a comprehensive *Guide to HMOs and Health Insurers* that includes a complete list of ratings for every company. This reference book is available as an annual or quarterly publication, and while it is too expensive for an individual to buy, a large public library might carry it.

Your insurance agent should also be able to provide you with the ratings that A.M. Best and Weiss Ratings have assigned to each company from which you are considering buying a policy. It is also important to check these ratings every year or so *after* you buy a policy.

What You Should Ask the Insurance People Before You Buy

A policy may look good on paper, but if the company refuses for one reason or another to pay the promised benefit, or if benefits come so slowly that they cause you worry, inconvenience, and embarrassment, you may want to avoid that policy—no matter how low the premiums or how high the supposed coverage. Therefore, you should investigate the claims response record of the company before you purchase a policy. The important facts are generally not published, and you may need to ask the insurance agent the following questions:

- **What is the loss ratio on the policy (or on a similar policy if the policy you are considering is new) for the past few years?** This figure may differ from the "anticipated loss ratio" usually cited in promotional literature. If the actual figure is much lower than the anticipated figure, ask why.

- **How long, on average, does it take to process a claim and for you or your doctor or hospital to receive payment?** It can be worrisome and costly if benefits arrive inordinately slowly. Ask where your claim will go and who has to approve it. Are authorizations made locally, or are all claims forwarded to the "head office"?

- **What percentage of claims is reduced and what percentage is denied on the policy you are investigating? Why have such claims been reduced or denied?** The overwhelming majority of insurers have scrupulous claims procedures, but a few have been known to try to cut losses through legal challenges to claims. You want to be certain that any policy you purchase will pay benefits promptly as promised.

- **What are your rights as a policyholder if your claim is reduced or denied?**

- **Is the claim form straightforward and simple, or overly complex?** Ask to see a copy if you will be required to file it yourself (see next paragraph).

79

- **Who will be paid benefits, you or the health care provider?** Generally, you save time and trouble if the company will pay the doctor directly. Many doctors have arrangements with insurers so that you need not bother filing claim forms. Others have no such arrangements, and you must take care of the bills and file for your insurance benefits. If you are still ill when the bills start to come in, this task can be burdensome.

- **If the company will pay benefits directly to the health care provider, how will you be notified that payments have been made?** This is important, since all too often the doctor's office will mistakenly continue to bill you for charges already paid by your insurance. You need evidence that the bill has been paid. Also, the absence of notification will alert you that the company may not have paid the bill.

- **How are claims for treatment out-of-state or outside your "prevailing charges area" evaluated?** Many insurance companies calculate premiums based on actuarial estimates for a limited geographical area. Some of them will pay only the "prevailing charges" of your area even though the charges in other areas may be higher, leaving you at substantial risk. For example, if you reside in a rural or suburban area and are stricken with an illness that requires emergency surgery in a large metropolitan area, the difference in coverage from one "prevailing charge" area to the other could easily amount to hundreds, if not thousands of dollars. The incidence of illness among seniors is statistically greater during holiday visits with relatives and friends than at other times. You certainly want to be protected during those times.

Your questioning may very well make the insurance representative uncomfortable, but it is your right and in your interest to ask. If the salesperson is uncooperative or if he is pleasant but never provides you the information you want, do not do business with that person.

Open Enrollment Requirement

The NAIC Medicare Model legislation requires that new Medicare subscribers be allowed a six-month "open enrollment" period in which they cannot be denied Medicare supplemental insurance because of their health status, previous claims history, or medical condition. Section 11 of the NAIC Model Standards provisions states: "No issuer of Medicare supplement policies in this state may deny or condition the issuance or effectiveness of any Medicare supplement policy available for sale in this state, nor may it discriminate in the pricing of such policy because of the health status, claims experience, receipt of health care, or medical condition of an applicant where an application for such policy is submitted during the six (6) month period beginning with the first month in which an individual (who is 65 years of age or older) first enrolled for benefits under Medicare Part B." Most states now have adopted such legislation.

Take advantage of this window of opportunity. If you do not, you may not be able to get the policy you want, may face a pre-existing-condition limitation, may have to pay more for any given policy, or may even run the risk of not being able to buy a policy at all. This point cannot be overemphasized—**once you sign up for Medicare Part B, make sure you do not inadvertently miss the six-month open-enrollment period for purchasing a Medicare Supplement insurance policy.**

What You Should Tell the Insurance People Before You Buy

Even with the open enrollment guarantee, the medical history that you will be required to submit when applying for a policy constitutes an integral part of the insurance contract. If that medical history can be demonstrated to have been willfully falsified, the insurance contract may not be legally binding.

It is therefore crucial that you complete the medical history form accurately. Do not be concerned about reporting illness that required hospitalization, surgery, or other treatment in the past. A person who reaches age 65 with no prior history of illness is the exception, not the rule.

Do not think that because you may not have to submit to a physical examination, your health history is not of consequence to the insurance company. It is. That is why the health history you complete becomes a part of the contract.

Even though you may sign a contract, pay premiums, and be issued a policy, an incorrect health history could mean that you have absolutely no insurance.

Unfortunately, all too many of the claims difficulties retired people have reported in the past were their own fault. Policyholders have paid hundreds and hundreds of dollars in premiums only to have their claims legally denied by the insurance company when illness struck. In most of these cases, the claimants either gave false information or withheld pertinent information of which they had knowledge when they completed their applications for insurance.

Therefore, answer all questions regarding your health honestly and completely. This does not mean that you will be required to recall everything that happened to you in the past. But as a matter of contractual integrity, you are obliged to do the best you can. To do otherwise places you at enormous risk.

IX.

RANKING MEDIGAP POLICIES BY COST AND RISK

D ESPITE the "simplification" of medigap insurance through the NAIC's delineation of ten standard policies, it can still be difficult to determine which policy offers the best value for a particular individual. Of course, the task of comparing similar policies has been made immeasurably easier—other things being equal, for identical policies the one with the lowest premium is the best value. But that type of comparison does not determine which options might be most valuable to individual consumers. Indeed, advice about the value of different coverage options often is vague and subjective. Although we know of no foolproof way to evaluate the relative values of the health insurance policies now on the market, we try here to provide a procedure that can be applied to virtually anyone's circumstance.

Many state insurance departments or related state agencies (see Chapter VIII) provide booklets to help you compare the NAIC supplemental policies. These usually include two or three pages of comparison worksheets for you to fill in policy options and compare prices. The guide *Choosing a Medigap Policy*, which is available through the national Medicare hotline at 1-800-MEDICARE (1-800-633-4227) or on the Medicare website at www.medicare.gov, walks you through six "steps to buying a medigap policy" and includes three worksheets. These guides advise you to "weigh each option carefully" and to "decide which is best for you." Unfortunately, they usually do not tell you *how* to weigh options or *how* to arrive at an informed decision regarding them. With little or no help, you are asked to compare different options whose value to you remains unknown. Here we try to be more specific.

When evaluating health insurance, risk and cost should be your overriding concerns. Since the purpose of health insurance is to reduce financial risk, you must determine the extent to which any given policy would reduce this risk in the event of illness. Next, you must answer how much you will have to pay for this protection.

The cost-risk principle helps you to elect insurance that provides the most protection against risk at the lowest cost. The following is a simple expression of this principle, which we shall call the "cost-risk index," that allows you to compare the relative value of policies:

Cost-Risk Index = Cost x Risk

Cost is the annual premium on the policy. Many insurance companies quote monthly, quarterly, or semiannual premiums to make the amount seem more affordable. To convert these to an annual figure: multiply monthly amounts by 12, multiply quarterly premiums by 4, and multiply semiannual premiums by 2.

Risk is the amount you would owe for medical care after both Medicare and the supplemental policy had paid their benefits. To determine risk, design a hypothetical situation or situations in which you assume the need for a certain type of care and then calculate how much protection a policy would not provide in the event of such need. Although time-consuming, this is the most useful and least complicated way of calculating risk.

Obviously, the lower the *cost* and the lower the *risk,* the lower the *cost-risk index* and the better the value. A higher index indicates a poorer value.

Advantages of Multiple-Case Evaluation of Risk

Previous uses of hypothetical cases in the evaluation of Medicare supplemental insurance have relied mainly on a single-case risk design. That is, the determination of risk was based on only one hypothetical situation. Although a single-case design has some value and is not very time-consuming to develop, a multiple-case risk design can be more useful.

Multiple-case risk designs incorporate both the strengths and weaknesses in coverage over a number of policy provisions. (Single-case designs of necessity exclude one or more provisions from determination of risk.) Further, these designs allow flexibility and weighting. For instance, you can accommodate *average risks* based on the reported experience of the Medicare population, infrequent but potentially *catastrophic risks,* and the likelihood of *known risks* based on your own health history.

A wide variety of potentially ruinous illnesses require many different types of care—and hence insurance coverage. Thus the value of multiple-case designs, unlike single-case designs, can account for a number of potential risks.

The following risk design was determined after consultation with health care planners and with reference to the *Activity Reports* of the Commission on Professional and Hospital Activities. It incorporates both average risk experience and potential risk experience. Adhering to the health insurance principle, weight has been given to the potential risks. This design may be used as shown or adjusted to accommodate your own health situation:

Sample Risk Design

Case 1: Average Hospital Confinement
5-day hospitalization
Medical expense of $7,500

Case 2: Intermediate Hospital Confinement/
Intermediate Skilled Nursing Facility Confinement
21-day hospitalization
30-day skilled nursing facility confinement
Medical expense of $25,000

´ Case 3: Extended Hospital Confinement
100-day hospitalization
Medical expense of $85,000

Case 4: Extended Skilled Nursing Facility Confinement
16-day hospitalization
180-day skilled nursing facility confinement
Medical expense of $35,000

Case 5: Extended Hospital Confinement/
Extended Skilled Nursing Facility Confinement
180-day hospitalization
150-day skilled nursing facility confinement
Medical expense of $200,000

To determine the total risk associated with this risk design for each policy you are considering: (1) calculate probable daily hospital and skilled nursing facility costs for your locality by calling the billing department of your hospital or local nursing facility and requesting current daily charges; (2) calculate what you would still owe after the insurance benefits had been paid for each case; and then (3) sum these five amounts. That is your total estimated financial risk.

This "Sample Risk Design" accommodates a variety of hypothetical situations based on a distribution of both *potential* and *average* risks. However, it was figured *without* regard to individual health experience, which can have a significant bearing on the value of a particular policy. For persons whose health history indicates no particular risk, the sample risk design will indicate how different policies compare in relation to average risk experience; absent prior knowledge of illness or the likelihood of illness, averages permit a statistical assessment of intermediate risks. However, potential risks based on your own health history must always receive the greatest weight in the multiple-case evaluation of risk.

Your health history may suggest that your risks in some areas are greater than in others. If you know of an existing condition, or have parents and relatives who have been stricken with an illness requiring specific care, then you should use this knowledge to your advantage. If, for example, you or members of your family are prone to illness requiring long-term care in a skilled nursing facility, then your design ought to include such a hypothetical case. Or if you or members of your immediate family suffer from a chronic condition that requires regular physician visits and treatment, but not hospitalization or skilled nursing facility confinement, then your risk design ought to give more weight to that condition.

If you include potential risks in your risk design, then you can weight your evaluation toward your individual health risks. For the most part, however, this is a matter of "fine tuning" and is not likely to affect greatly the rank order of policies. In cases where there is a close decision to be made, however, it may suggest the more attractive alternative.

Using the Cost-Risk Index

In order to compare the relative values of specific policies, calculate the cost-risk index for each by multiplying the total risk as determined above by the annual premium amount.

The resulting cost-risk index rank (the indexes listed by magnitude) must be interpreted with discretion. It does not *prove* that one policy represents a "better value" than another. Rather, the index rank provides you only with one statistical indication of how different policies may or may not represent value in view of your own needs and resources.

Such indexes and rankings do, however, broadly indicate relative value. A policy with a relatively low cost-risk index *usually* means that it is a good value. Risk is by far the larger factor in the cost-risk formula, so that a low index nearly always indicates low risk. Low price and low risk determine good value. A policy with an intermediate index value might indicate any of several situations: (1) risk might be low, but price is high; (2) price might be low, but risk is relatively high; or (3) both price and risk are moderate.

A policy with a high index, however, *usually* indicates poor value. Either the risk is high, or the cost is high, or both. In general, the lower the cost-risk index, the better the value.

Part 3
LONG-TERM CARE OPTIONS

X.
LONG-TERM CARE INSURANCE

FOR many years long-term care was synonymous with nursing home care. That has never been entirely accurate, and in the past decade the link between the two has weakened further. Not all long-term care is provided in nursing homes, and not all care provided in nursing homes is long-term.

Long-term care is not a single, unified service, but is made up of many different support services aimed at helping people who have lost some capacity for self-care because of a cognitive or chronic condition or illness. These patients require the help of others to perform what are referred to as "activities of daily living." These include eating, bathing, toileting, dressing, transferring (getting out of a bed, a chair, etc.) and continence. Such care is expensive and can easily cost $50,000 per year or more.

Medicare does not cover long-term custodial care in nursing homes, in assisted living facilities or at home. Medicaid, the government health program for the poor, does cover nursing home care, but has strict eligibility requirements, including income and asset limits. Simply put, impoverishment is a prerequisite for participation in the Medicaid program.

Will You Need Nursing Home Care?

Older Americans understandably fear the prospect of being unable to care for themselves and to live independently. These fears are fueled by literature sent out by insurance companies to promote their long-term care policies. The brochures cite frightening statistics that imply that there is a high likelihood that individuals will require long-term care in a nursing home. Among the widely-cited claims that we have seen: "nearly 40 percent of people age 65 now are likely to spend some time in a nursing home," "the average length of stay in a nursing home is nearly three years," and "half of all women and a third of all men who are now over 65 will spend their last years in a nursing home."

However, statements like this exaggerate the probability of requiring long-term nursing home care. They may frighten some people into buying a policy, but far fewer Americans are confined for as many years in nursing homes as insurance salespeople would have you believe.

It is beyond the scope of this discussion to consider all the factors involved in estimating the risk that one may need *any* long-term care. However, inasmuch as current long-term care insurance sales efforts may focus on such care *in a nursing home*, and may be directed at those consumers who are least apt to require such care, it may be useful to review the characteristics of nursing home residents as reported in public and private sources.

Surveys of nursing home utilization by the Department of Health and Human Services' National Center for Health Statistics (NCHS) have generally been regarded as the most accurate measures to date of the risks of the elderly of needing care in such a facility. The NCHS's latest National Nursing Home Survey (1999) provides estimates of nursing home facilities, current residents, and discharges. Perhaps the most explosive statistics to come out of the NCHS are that about two in five persons over age 65 will require nursing home care at some time in their lives and that, on average, those now in nursing homes have been confined for nearly two and a half years. Taken together, these statistics have been cited by healthcare activists and insurance salespeople alike as evidence that the elderly face a very substantial risk of confinement for many years in a nursing home.

Such a conclusion is unwarranted. Even though as many as 40 percent of today's elderly *may* at some time require care in a nursing home, the overwhelming number of nursing home admissions result in short stays. The latest NCHS survey of "discharges" from nursing homes, which includes patients that died, shows that more than two-thirds of all discharges (68.3 percent) were for stays of less than three months, and slightly more than four-fifths (83.2 percent) of all discharged patients had been confined for under a year. Indeed, patients who had been confined for three years or longer represented only 7.4 percent of all discharges.

What accounts for the seeming discrepancy between these two sets of data? The NCHS survey of nursing home residents is based on a *population* census. A census counts only those who reside at a given place at the time the census is taken. It says nothing about those who may have lived there previously or about those who will

92

live there at some future time. The NCHS survey of nursing home discharges, on the other hand, is a rough record of the "flow" of patients over a specified time period, and includes the experience of short-term patients. Although it is far from clear that the available discharge data are representative of the "average" nursing home experience of the elderly (if there is such a thing), they plainly indicate that the risks of long-term confinement have been far less than might be inferred from the NCHS survey of nursing home residents.

The nursing home residency pattern may illustrate a phenomenon that is common to virtually any institution that has certain population limits. Stated simply, nursing homes tend to generate *populations* of long-term residents. The reason is uncomplicated, but an illustration may be helpful. Assume, for example, that a nursing home has 50 beds and that initially it admits patients with a wide range of clinical problems. Of those initial 50, 20 die within a few weeks of admission and 25 return home, leaving five still in residence and 45 beds available. Of the 45 "new" patients, assume that 20 die and 20 go home—but five remain, enlarging the number of long-term residents to ten and leaving only 40 beds available. The process continues until most beds are occupied by long-term patients. Unless an institution specifically reserves a percentage of its beds for "transients," over time almost all beds in a given facility will become occupied by long-term patients. While the NCHS nursing home population censuses confirm this circumstance, they reveal nothing about the experiences of the vastly greater number of patients who were discharged after short stays, or about those who never were admitted to a nursing home at all.

This process is also characteristic of organizations as diverse as social or athletic clubs, which tend to become more exclusive because openings become available only as current members die; academic departments in colleges and universities that confer lifetime tenure, which become bloated with senior faculty; and prisons, which tend to become populated mainly with "lifers" as lesser felons serve out their time and are paroled while the incorrigibles remain incarcerated (which accounts for the fact that even though crime rates may not accelerate, prison "shortages" still occur).

Although nursing home residency data may give an exaggerated sense of the likelihood of spending a long time in a nursing home, they are useful for the light they shed on some key characteristics of those requiring long-term institutional care. Even though long-term care insurance sales promotions often target married men, the data suggest that this group represents only a small fraction of those receiving long-term care *in nursing homes.* Women over 65 far outnumber men over 65 in nursing homes, and unmarried (single or widowed) patients outnumber married ones by an even greater margin (almost nine to one, according to data from the 1980s). The incidence of nursing home confinement for *unmarried* (single or widowed) men over 65 is about twice the incidence for married men over 65, but the former are outnumbered by unmarried women four to one. Indeed, unmarried women (single or widowed) constitute by far the largest category of long-term nursing home patients.

The likelihood that either spouse will require long-term care during the early years of retirement is very slight. In 1999, only 1.1 percent of men and women aged 65-74 years were confined in a nursing home. Among *married* persons aged 65-74, nursing home residency rates are minuscule: around 0.2 percent of the population in that age group.

The chances that nursing home care will be needed increase markedly with age. Of those aged 75-84 years, about 3.1 percent of men and 5.1 percent of women were receiving nursing home care in 1999. However, nursing home residency jumps sharply among those 85 years and older. Of those elderly, about one in nine men and one in five women resided in nursing homes in 1999.

Moreover, the medical data suggest that mental condition may now be a key factor, if not *the* key factor, in a majority of nursing home admissions. According to a 1985 NCHS survey, nursing home patients suffered from a variety of physical ills that are listed as the "primary diagnosis." However, even the most common of these diagnoses, heart disease and cerebrovascular disease, were represented by only 17 percent and 11 percent, respectively, of all nursing home residents.

Mental deterioration, on the other hand, was a far more prevalent condition: "Overall, 66 percent of all nursing home residents were reported to have at least one of the following conditions: mental retardation, alcohol abuse or dependence, drug abuse or dependence, senile dementia or chronic and organic brain syndrome, depressive disorders, schizophrenia, other psychoses, anxiety disorders, personality or character disorders, or other mental disorders." Of the two-thirds of residents who were mentally impaired, the vast majority (87 percent) when interviewed were found "to have one or more behavioral problems: disrobing or exposing oneself, screaming, being physically abusive to self or others, stealing, getting lost or wandering into unacceptable places, or inability to avoid simple dangers...underscoring the increasing role of nursing homes in caring for the chronically mentally ill...Cognitive impairment and behavioral problems have been cited as reasons for nursing home admission."

In short, the characteristics of long-term nursing home residents tend to be far more specific than might be implied by popular discussions of the "long-term care crisis." Many of the elderly may have one or more physical conditions that prevent them from being totally independent. According to government statistics, nearly one-seventh of the nation's seniors—over five million people—have a limitation in either one or more activities of daily living (such as preparing food, housekeeping, and handling finances). But this does not necessarily mean that they all will end up in nursing homes. A spouse, family relations, friends, or a variety of home care or community-based services for seniors often can provide the required help. Alternative housing arrangements, such as assisted living, may also be sufficient. In these circumstances, most older people with disabilities apparently can manage in a non-nursing home setting, provided they have use of their mental faculties. This experience applies especially to elderly married men, who often are cared for by wives who can be expected, in statistical terms, to outlive them.

In contrast, most nursing home admissions that result in long-term stays would seem to be those of aged unmarried men and women (mostly women)—without family or friends to care for them, usually because mental impairment and associated behavioral problems have made them dangerous to themselves or difficult to care for.

Nursing Homes In Perspective

The nursing home is a relatively modern creation that evolved mainly as a result of two concurrent developments: the advent of modern antibiotics that increased life expectancies remarkably, and increased "middle class" affluence that followed World War II. Prior to that time, care for the elderly infirm usually was provided either through family or through numerous voluntary organizations, charities, and churches that sponsored "old folks homes." In most cases, the burden of such care probably was less than might be imagined today. Most elderly people who subsequently contracted serious illnesses—pneumonia or some other infectious disease—died, and the caregiver was relieved of further responsibility. By contrast, postwar medical advances, most notably antibiotics and other drugs, kept such people alive but often in physical circumstances that did not permit them to live independently. A parent might recover from a serious illness and require more care than ever. The absence of support services to help family caregivers, the nursing home provided an increasingly efficient solution.

More recent progress in medical technology (artificial joints, bypass surgery, organ transplants, drug therapy, eye surgery, and the like) may be reversing that trend by enabling many older people whose conditions formerly would have made them nursing home candidates to continue to manage their own lives. With increasing availability of home care services and assisted-living housing arrangements, a primary concern of many elderly with disabilities may not be how long they will be confined in a nursing home, but rather how best to manage the many other services that are available to them. The period of absolute dependency, when institutionalization may be necessary, seems very likely to shrink—possibly dramatically.

Trends in nursing home usage suggest that older persons may already be living in the community longer and entering nursing homes later and more dependent (due to physical or cognitive problems) than before. Between 1995 and 2001, the number of nursing home residents decreased by more than 10,000. Options such as home health care, assisted living, and continuing care retirement communities are helping to drive this trend. In 2000, there were about 800,000 individuals living in assisted living facilities, a 30 percent increase from 1998. Visiting nurses, hospice care, physical therapy, respite care, and other community resources aid also informal caregivers, allowing the elderly to remain home longer.

Unless the number of new beds grows markedly, an aging population may increasingly limit *long-term* nursing home space to those with the greatest dependencies, mostly the chronically mentally ill. Nursing homes may in effect become surrogate mental institutions— a process that to some extent probably already has been accelerated by the deinstitutionalization of mental patients—while long-term care for the remaining elderly is routinely provided by other means.

In short, the market for nursing home care and elder care is not immune to change. Rather, the pace of change in medicine and support services virtually guarantees that things will *not* stay as they are. It remains to be seen if consumer demand for nursing home care already may have peaked. But, given the uncertainties, a narrowly written long-term care policy that promises to pay benefits only in a nursing-home setting would seem to offer little comfort. Most people clearly would be better off, if they decide to buy a policy, to buy one that covers care outside of a nursing home.

Long-Term Care Insurance

Many of the early long-term care insurance policies covered only nursing home care. They were very high-priced indemnity contracts (contracts that pay a fixed-dollar amount per day) that provided limited coverage far below that required for protection against the catastrophic costs of long-term custodial care. In the past decade, however, some of the most objectionable features of earlier policies, such as those requiring prior hospitalization before admission to a nursing home or excluding coverage for nursing care required for Alzheimer's disease, have been eliminated.

Moreover, many policies now cover not only care in a nursing home, but also care provided at home or in an assisted living facility. Care provided in such settings can help people to postpone or avoid entering a nursing home. In this respect, perhaps the best argument for purchasing a long-term care insurance policy is to provide re-sources to help you avoid going into a nursing home.

Older policies purchased at an earlier age may still have valuable benefits for an individual and should be reviewed carefully before they are replaced. If you want to add additional modifications to an existing policy, keep in mind that your existing policy was pur-chased at an earlier age and should be less expensive than a similar policy at an older age. Therefore, it may be cost-effective to keep your existing policy with its limitations, and add additional benefits with a second policy, such as a home care only policy.

Despite improvements, long-term care insurance is still one of the most complicated insurance products on the market.

Benefit Triggers

The degree of impairment that triggers benefits varies widely. Insurers usually begin paying benefits when you become unable to perform two or more of the activities of daily living (ADLs, as they are referred to by the healthcare industry). *The six ADLS used to determine if one is eligible for benefits are eating, bathing, toileting, dressing, transferring (getting out of a bed, a chair, etc.) and continence.* In addition, most policies provide benefits for cognitive impairment. However, the list of covered ADLs may vary from one policy to the next. Some cover all six ADLs, others cover only five. The ADL usually excluded by the latter policies – bathing - is one of the most important. According to healthcare researchers, bathing is usually the first ADL that a person cannot do. Thus, qualifying for benefits from a policy that uses only five ADLs may be difficult if bathing is not one of the five.

The standards for judging impairment also vary among insurance companies. Some policies pay benefits only if you need "substantial assistance." For example, someone has to dress you. Others require only that you need "hands-on" assistance (someone to button your shirt). The most generous require only that you need "standby assistance" to qualify for benefits (someone within arm's reach while you dress yourself). Some insurers pay benefits if your doctor certifies that the care is medically necessary, regardless of cognitive limitations or ability to perform ADLs.

Daily Benefits

Most long-term care policies promise to pay only a fixed amount of benefits for a limited period of time. Insurers normally pay benefits by the day, week, or month. They let you choose an amount that ranges from, say, $50 to $350 per day, $350 to $2,450 per week, or $1,500 to $10,500 per month. Most policies limit the total benefit they will pay over the life of the policy to a maximum number of dollars or days. For example, you might be covered for one, two, or three years of benefits. Some policies offer lifetime coverage, but this option is expensive. As you would expect, the more risk you protect, the higher your premium.

The dollar value of the home health care benefit normally is half of the nursing home benefit (*e.g.*, $50 per day vs. $100 per day). Keep in mind, however, that home care is *not* necessarily less expensive than care in a nursing home. If a person becomes substantially impaired, he might well need round-the-clock care or supervision. In this situation, a modest home care insurance benefit might be sufficient *if* family and friends are available to fill in the gaps. In the absence of such caregivers, however, the individual would need a much larger home care benefit in order to stay out of a nursing home. Before buying a policy, you should consider whether the benefit you can afford will be adequate.

In addition to nursing home coverage and home health care, policies may (or may not) cover respite care, hospice care, services in assisted living facilities, services in adult day-care centers, or services in other community facilities. Home care usually is limited to care from licensed nurses or certified nurse's aides, who are hired either independently or through licensed agencies. However, some policies pay for care from unlicensed aides or may pay for broader "homemaker" services (such as cooking or cleaning).

Elimination or Waiting Periods

Once benefits are triggered, payments will not actually begin until after an elimination period (also called the deductible or waiting period). The longer the elimination period, the lower your premium will be, all else equal. For example, if you choose a policy with an elimination period of 100 days, you will pay a lower premium than if the elimination period were 50 days.

Reimbursement vs. Indemnity

Most long-term care policies are "reimbursement" contracts. This means that they pay for each specific service received or expense incurred up to a preset limit. This is one way to ensure that when a policy holder needs care, he or she receives care from a qualified provider approved by the insurer.

Some insurers issue "indemnity" policies, which pay a set dollar amount directly to the policy holder as long as he or she meets the benefit trigger. Some indemnity policies pay even if you are not receiving any long-term care services; you decide how to spend your money. For example, you can pay a relative or neighbor to provide care rather than having to go through a licensed home-health-care agency that is approved by the insurance company. However, indemnity policies are usually more expensive than reimbursement policies. The latter pay benefits under more restrictive conditions; these restrictions are designed to limit claims, which may help to avoid future rate increases.

NAIC Minimum Standards

In contrast to medigap insurance, long-term care insurance policies are *not* standardized. However, since the 1980s the National Association of Insurance Commissioners (NAIC) has recommended policy guidelines to protect consumers and limit complexity in the long-term care insurance market. Many states require policies to adhere to the NAIC's "model regulation" and some states have adopted even stricter regulations. Thus, a review of the model's major provisions should give you a better understanding of long-term care insurance and the issues to consider when shopping for a policy. According to the NAIC, all long-term care insurance policies should provide at least the following:

- Definitions of terms should be stated clearly in the policy. In addition, a complete description of all "covered" providers of services, especially their licensure or certification requirements or degree status, must be included in the contract. A number of policies have failed to pay claims because the care received did not meet the technical definition of "covered" care. For example, policyholders have had benefits withheld because the care provider was not licensed by the state, as required by the policy; still others have had their claims denied because the facility did not meet the company's criteria, which were not stated in the policy.

- All policies must be "guaranteed renewable." That is, you may continue your policy by timely payment of premiums—the insurer cannot decrease coverage or increase premiums on you *individually* due to age or physical condition. However, the premium *rate* is *not* guaranteed. The insurer may raise the premium rates in the future for a class of policies, which could include yours. For those on fixed incomes, this could make policies prohibitively expensive. Companies that are financially troubled or facing larger-than-expected claims may be more likely to raise premiums. Before buying a policy, check the company's financial standing and ask about the history of any rate increases.

- Striving to stabilize premiums, NAIC regulations now require insurers to certify the adequacy of their rates using actuarial models. Under the previous regulation, companies were required to use a 60 percent loss-ratio (the ratio of claims to premiums) as a basis to calculate rates for long-term care insurance policies. For example, an initial 60 percent loss-ratio requirement means that if the claims were expected to be $600, then the premium could not be greater than $1,000 (600/1000 = 0.6). This loss-ratio method artificially limited initial premiums and created an incentive for insurers to increase claims later on so they could raise rates. Under the new amendments, there is no fixed loss-ratio requirement on initial rate filings, but penalties will be imposed in the future if there are substantial rate increases. Some states have enacted additional limits on rate increases.

- To protect policyholders against substantial rate increases, insurers must offer them the option to purchase "nonforfeiture benefits." These benefits are triggered after a lapse or nonpayment on a policy. If the premium increase of a lapsed policy exceeds a certain percentage (based on age) the policyholder may (1) pay the higher premium for the same level of coverage; (2) pay the same premium for a decrease in the level of coverage; or (3) convert the coverage to a paid-up status (no more premiums) with a shortened benefit period. In each of these cases underwriting is prohibited. According to the Health Insurance Association of America, a nonforfeiture benefit can add 20 to 100 percent to a policy's cost.

- Insurers must offer policyholders the option to purchase "inflation protection." This option is crucial because the costs of long-term care are increasing faster than the rate of general price inflation. Thus, the nominal benefits offered by a policy may be woefully inadequate to cover the actual costs of care when it is needed. For instance, a nursing home that cost $153 a day in 2001 (the national average cost for that year) will cost $406 a day in 20 years if nursing home costs rise five percent annually.

Most policies with inflation protection automatically increase benefits each year by a fixed compound percentage, usually five percent. If price inflation accelerates, even this "protection" would prove inadequate. In that case, a provision that guarantees to pay a specified percentage of actual charges and has no dollar limit would provide better inflation protection. Some policies provide a guaranteed right to increase benefit levels periodically without providing evidence of insurability. Again, this feature comes at a cost. Inflation protection can boost premiums 40 percent to over 100 percent, depending on the option you select.

- Limitations and exclusions of coverage may be permitted only for pre-existing conditions or diseases; mental or nervous disorders, other than Alzheimer's disease or other dementia; alcoholism or drug addiction; illness or injury caused by an act of war, service in the armed forces, attempted suicide, or intentionally self-inflicted injury; services provided in a government facility and for which benefits are available under Medicare or other government program; and services received abroad. Carefully review any exclusions that apply to policies you are considering. Be sure that the definitions of excluded coverage are specific and that you clearly understand them. If you have any questions about what is or is not covered, ask the agent for a clarification *in writing*. If you decide to purchase the policy, any such written documents should be kept with it.

- A group long-term care policy should be convertible to an individual policy with comparable coverage for a period of 31 days following the discontinuation of group insurance. The policyholder must have been continuously insured under the group plan for at least six months. Most long-term care policies are sold to individuals, but you can buy group coverage through an employer or through membership in an association. If your employment ends or your employer cancels the group plan, most states require that the converted coverage provide "substantially similar" benefits and premiums.

- No insurer may engage in "post-claims underwriting." Many policyholders have complained of insurance companies reviewing their health histories only *after* a claim had been filed. Insurers have denied claims and refunded the premiums paid into these policies if they deemed the health histories inadequate. To prevent this practice, NAIC requires that a number of provisions be added to the medical history application and that insurers accept such medical histories before or at the time the policy is issued.

- Long-term care insurance sales representatives are prohibited from making misleading representations; from using high-pressure tactics such as force, fright, or threat, whether explicit or implicit; and from employing "cold-lead advertising," which hides the real purpose of the solicitation—to sell insurance. Agents must review a personal worksheet with each applicant to determine suitability of benefits in each case and whether the applicant will be able to afford the policy if premiums increase or income becomes fixed or decreases. In addition, each applicant must be given a copy of the NAIC's *Shopper's Guide to Long-Term Care Insurance*. Of course, there will always be pushy salespeople, some of whom may employ shady sales tactics. If any insurance representative says you must "sign right away" or the policy will not be available, walk away. Consider purchasing a policy only after you have had the chance to review its provisions (in private and with the counsel of knowledgeable third parties) and to compare its costs and benefits with a number of other policies.

To repeat, long-term care insurance policies are not standardized. There are no "plans A through J" for you to compare, as there are with medigap insurance. Although the NAIC model does establish some minimum standards, it has not been adopted in every state. Moreover, it does not prescribe the specific benefits that a long-term policy must offer. Thus, even a policy that claims to adhere to the NAIC model may not provide adequate coverage.

Tax-Qualified Policies

Some long-term care policies meet special standards in order to qualify for favorable Federal tax treatment.

The Health Insurance Portability and Accountability Act of 1996 allows you to deduct from your taxable income all or part of the premiums that you pay for "tax-qualified" long-term care insurance.

In addition, the benefits you receive on such policies will not be counted as taxable income. In contrast, the benefits paid by non-tax-qualified policies may or may not be taxable; the IRS has not yet ruled on the matter.

Policies that are sold as "tax qualified" must meet certain standards. They must be "guaranteed renewable" (see page 100) and they must cover only "qualified long-term care services." In addition, a tax-qualified policy will pay a claim only if you are expected to need care for at least 90 days. To trigger benefits, you must require "substantial assistance" with at least two activities of daily living, or require "substantial supervision" due to severe cognitive impairment such as Alzheimer's disease or dementia.

In short, the benefit triggers for tax-qualified policies may be more restrictive than for non-tax-qualified policies, and the policies cover only periods of need that are expected to be relatively long-term, i.e., more than three months. The goal of these Federal standards is to encourage the purchase of policies that limit claims for short-term rehabilitations but do provide coverage for people with substantial problems who need longer-term care. The latter situation has the greatest potential to be financially catastrophic.

Policies purchased after January 1, 1997 may or may not be tax-qualified, depending on how they are written (ask your insurance agent). However, if you bought a policy *before* that date it probably is tax-qualified, since the tax law allowed many older policies to be considered qualified (grandfathered) even though they may not meet all of the standards described above.

If you own a tax-qualified policy, your premiums are deductible only under limited circumstances. Under Federal tax law, the portion of your medical expenses that exceeds 7.5 percent of your adjusted gross income may be deductible from your taxable income. To take advantage of this deduction you must itemize your deductions, which makes sense only if your total deductions are more than your standard deduction. Only certain medical expenses are deductible; for a list, check IRS Publication 17, *Your Federal Income Tax*.

You may count the premiums that you pay for a tax-qualified policy as part of these medical expenses. The maximum premium amount that you can deduct increases with age. The maximum deductions for 2004 are shown below. (These amounts increase annually based on the increase in the Medical Consumer Price Index.)

Age	Maximum Tax Deduction for Long-Term Care Insurance Premiums (2004)
40 or below	$ 260
41-50	490
51-60	980
61-70	2,600
71 or older	3,250

Note that, like many deductions, these tax savings may be more apparent than real. For example, a person with an adjustable gross income of $50,000 will only be able to deduct the portion of qualified medical expenses that exceeds $3,750 (7.5 percent of income). Of course, some seniors face substantial out-of-pocket expenses (for Medicare premiums, prescription drugs, dental services, etc.) and therefore might benefit from substantial tax savings on the cost of long-term care insurance premiums.

Guidelines for an Adequate Policy

Deciding which features of a long-term care insurance policy matter most is not easy. The NAIC standards discussed earlier provide useful guidelines, and the tax-qualified policies described above meet another set of standards. Another guide to useful features is the "model policy" recommended by the Partnership for Long-Term Care.

This Partnership is the result of a joint effort by the Robert Wood Johnson Foundation and four states (California, Connecticut, Indiana, and New York) to increase the use of private rather than public resources to pay for long-term care. These state Partnership programs provide incentives for seniors to purchase private long-term care insurance in return for the state's promise to waive Medicaid eligibility rules that normally require you to "spend down" your assets in order to have Medicaid pay for custodial nursing home costs when private insurance benefits cease. (For more information on these programs, see Chapter XII.)

Long-term care policies must meet minimum standards to qualify for these state Partnership programs. These standards are based on what researchers at the Robert Wood Johnson Foundation determined were essential features of a good long-term care insurance policy. As such, they may be helpful to anyone contemplating the purchase of a policy, regardless of whether they are eligible for these programs. The minimum standards for a Partnership policy purchased in New York are as follows:

- Duration: Each policy will cover a minimum of three years in a nursing home or six years of home care.

- Coverage Amount (minimum): In 2003, the minimum daily benefits were $163 for nursing home care and $82 for home care. (Note: The cost of health care is higher in New York than in many other states. A smaller benefit might be adequate in your state.)

- Elimination or Waiting Period: The elimination period for basic coverage is 100 days, but insurers may offer a shorter period for an additional premium.

- Services: Each policy must cover nursing home care, home health care, assisted living, adult day care, and care management.

- Other coverage features: Five percent inflation protection, compounded annually (inflation protection is optional for persons over the age of 80), level premiums and portability.

This coverage is not cheap. The average annual premium in 2003 for a basic New York Partnership plan with a 100-day elimination period was $1,395 at age 55, $2,348 at age 65 and $5,336 at age 75. These premiums underscore the need to carefully consider both your needs and your resources before investing in a long-term care policy. The premium for adequate coverage may be substantial.

Only the "Hale and Hearty" Need Apply

For those who already have serious health problems or will soon need long-term care services, it is usually too late to purchase a policy. To screen out high risks and keep their premiums competitive, insurers are very cautious and reject applicants they think are likely to make a claim. Thus, they usually reject anyone who needs help with any of the six activities of daily living or uses an assistive device such as a four-pronged cane.

A key part of the screening process is the applicant interview. For younger applicants, an insurer might conduct a telephone interview as part of their underwriting procedure. However, for older applicants, many insurers will send an examiner (usually a nurse or other health professional) to your home to evaluate your physical and mental condition. They evaluate your mobility and survey your ability to do basic activities such as bathing, toileting, dressing, and getting in and out of a chair. They also conduct various cognitive tests, such as word memory games and asking you to count backward by threes.

More subtly, the interviewers observe your demeanor, grooming, and living environment, looking for any indication of memory loss, confusion, or lack of mobility. They may ask to see your driver's license—not for identification purposes but because maintaining a license is a sign of mobility. They may ask you to show what prescriptions you are taking—partly to see if you have trouble remembering them.

You cannot avoid these tests; refusing to cooperate would be an automatic disqualifier. In the highly recommended book *J.K. Lasser's Choosing the Right Long-Term Care Insurance*, author Benjamin Lipson suggests ways to improve your performance. For example, schedule the interview at your best time of day, gather all your prescription bottles beforehand, and clean the house. Also, avoid making jokes to your doctors about "senior moments;" your offhand comments might show up in the medical notes the doctor must provide to the insurance company. (See page 111 for more information on Lipson's book.)

As already discussed, insurers also try to control their risks by carefully defining the conditions under which they will pay benefits and by promising to pay only a fixed amount for, in many cases, a limited period. However, most long-term care policies now cover a wider range of risks than they used to. Most now pay for home health, either as a basic benefit or an additional rider available for a higher premium. On the surface, this should substantially increase the appeal of long-term care insurance, since a great deal of long-term care is given at home or in other settings outside of nursing homes.

However, the home health care benefit is not usually sufficient to pay all of the costs for individuals who require round-the-clock assistance or supervision. The home care benefit is normally a fraction (generally half) of the daily benefit for nursing home confinement. But three shifts of full-time home care costs even more than it does at a nursing home. The home care benefit may be adequate if the insured can rely on a strong network of family and friends or assisted living to provide care the rest of the time. Otherwise, there would be too many gaps to fill.

Long-Term Care (Living Benefits) Life Insurance

Life insurance normally pays benefits only after you die; it is not designed to pay for health care. However, many life insurance companies now offer policyholders the option of taking their death benefits from life insurance policies *before* they die. This innovation was introduced in the United States in response to AIDS patients seeking additional financial resources to help cover medical costs. Since then, this provision has been expanded to cover most terminal illnesses and many catastrophic illnesses as well. The option is available in new policies or as a rider to existing ones.

The logic behind offering "living benefits" is simple. The insurance company eventually will have to pay death benefits to a terminally ill policyholder's beneficiary, and it makes little difference if they pay it slightly sooner rather than later. The cost to the insurer is minimal, representing only the potential interest earnings lost on the benefit when it is paid out, say, a year earlier. Insurers can make up this cost by paying a living benefit that is somewhat less than the face value of the policy. For the insured, accelerated benefits can help defray medical costs and reduce the financial upheaval that can follow even an expected death. Moreover, the insured could conceivably use the funds to finance lifesaving medical treatment.

The most conservative policies provide early death benefits only in the case of terminal illness. The living benefit is a percentage of the face value of the policy, typically ranging from 50 to 80 percent. Some insurers also offer accelerated benefits to cover long-term care or confinement in a nursing home, regardless of whether the patient is terminally ill. In these cases, the insured may be allowed to choose a monthly benefit rather than a lump sum. The monthly benefit is usually a percentage of the face value. For example, a $150,000

108

policy might pay two percent of the face value, or $3,000, per month. Since the fixed amount does not vary with the cost of care, the living benefit is similar to a hospital indemnity policy. Whether the insured chooses a lump sum or monthly benefits, he can elect the living benefits option only once, and the consent of the beneficiary may be required.

Policy provisions vary widely among companies. For example, some pay long-term "catastrophic" benefits only after the insured has been confined to a nursing home for three or even six months. Others pay these monthly benefits only if the insured is hospitalized prior to confinement in a nursing home (most nursing home residents do not require hospitalization). Others restrict the types of illnesses that qualify for benefits. The broadest coverage includes heart disease, life-threatening cancer, stroke, Alzheimer's disease, kidney failure, and liver failure. Most cover any illness that leaves the insured with a life expectancy of 12 months or less, although even this provision may vary among policies. Every diagnosis requires verification by a doctor. In addition to differences in coverage, the percentage of the face value paid in advance also varies from company to company.

The Health Insurance Portability and Accountability Act of 1996 eliminated the income tax on certain advanced payments of life insurance, including accelerated death benefits under a standard life insurance policy. For payments to avoid taxation, a chronically ill person must be certified by a licensed health care practitioner to be unable to perform at least two of six activities of daily living for at least 90 days. Persons who need to be supervised to protect their personal health or safety (*e.g.*, Alzheimer's patients) also fall under the standard. Accelerated benefit payments are tax-free only if they are paid under a rider or other contractual agreement as they would be under a long-term care insurance policy. The payments are not tax-free if an insured's long-term care is already being paid for by long-term care insurance or Medicaid. Consult a tax attorney or accountant for more specific advice on this tax issue.

Older people who might otherwise let their life insurance lapse (say, because their children have grown) might instead choose to keep it in force to take advantage of the availability of tax-free accelerated benefits. The cost of this simple rider is minimal, and some companies provide it at no extra charge. However, living benefits are not costless. The death benefit, the cash value, and the loan value of the policy all will be reduced if the insured takes advantage of the early benefits option. Most important, remember that the living benefits provided by a life insurance policy are no substitute for a comprehensive health insurance policy.

What Should You Do?

Long-term care insurance, as currently marketed, remains confusing. The cost of policies varies greatly, and it is often unclear why. In addition, consumers must struggle to understand and to be able to compare how benefits are paid, what services are covered, where services are covered, what is not covered, when and why benefits are triggered, and so forth. Although the policies may be less deceptive than they were a decade ago, they remain very complicated, making it difficult to know whether a policy is providing adequate protection.

Assuming you can decipher the fine print of the policy, you also have to be able to pay for it. Comprehensive long-term care contracts remain among the most expensive insurance products on the market. Affordability is even more of an issue for married couples, since spouses must purchase individual coverage. (To reduce this financial burden a bit, some insurers offer discounts to married couples when both purchase long-term care coverage.) Many prospective buyers will not be able to afford an adequate policy. They will be tempted to buy a cheaper policy whose benefits are too small or too limited to do much good. You should not buy a policy if you cannot afford the premiums or are not reasonably sure you can pay the premium for the rest of your life or until you need care.

In shopping for a policy, do your homework ahead of time; do not expect to get unbiased, accurate, and comprehensive information from an agent. One useful source is the *Shopper's Guide to Long-Term Care Insurance*, available free on request from the National Association of Insurance Commissioners, 2301 McGee, Suite 800, Kansas City, Missouri 64108-2604; (816) 842-3600; website at www.naic.org.

Also, check with your state Insurance Department (listed in Chapter VIII) for additional publications that may be available in your state. Some states require the Insurance Commissioner to prepare annually a consumer guide for long-term care insurance. These guides may include a list of companies selling policies in your state, the types of benefits and policies you can buy, and a rate history of each company.

In addition, *J. K. Lasser's Choosing the Right Long-Term Care Insurance,* by Benjamin Lipson (John Wiley and Sons, 2002, $16.95 softcover), is a very readable and comprehensive guide to purchasing long-term care insurance. Lipson, an independent insurance broker, describes how these policies work, what services are covered, how benefits are paid, and what to expect when you apply for a policy. He includes many real-life examples and practical advice, from a "list of questions insurance companies hope you never ask" to "finding a seller you can trust."

Also, get as much information as you can about the long-term care services and facilities you might use, including quality of care and how much they charge. When you are ready to begin investigating individual policies, check with several companies and agents. Be sure to compare benefits, the limits on your coverage, any exclusions, and premiums. Review the companies' rate increase histories. Choose only a financially sound insurance company.

Be sure you accurately complete your application. Your medical history is important. If the information is not accurate and complete and the insurer used the information to issue you the policy, the company can refuse to pay your claims and can even cancel your policy.

Whether you should buy a long-term care insurance policy will depend largely on your age, health history, overall retirement goals, family situation, income and assets, and the types of services and policies available in your area. After doing your investigating, you may decide not to buy a policy. But at least you will be making an informed decision and will have a better idea of what to consider if you want to make alternative arrangements for care.

XI.
LONG-TERM CARE ALTERNATIVES

P RESUMABLY, most of us would rather spend our final years in home surroundings of our own choosing rather than in an institutionalized setting that is forced on us. As discussed in the preceding chapter, the possibility that you will reside many years in a nursing home is quite small. Statistically, the vast majority of elderly Americans live out their lives in their own or in family members' homes, or in some other type of community setting.

This does not mean that many older people will never require assistance, perhaps substantial assistance, with their living arrangements, or decide to move to more convenient homes. Fortunately, a variety of alternatives to nursing homes are becoming increasingly available. Developments in medicine, support services, and demographics almost guarantee that the market for long-term care will continue to change.

In this chapter, we discuss three options—assisted living communities, continuing care retirement communities (CCRCs), and home health and elder care—that have become widely used alternatives to conventional nursing home care.

Assisted Living Communities

Assisted living communities have proliferated in recent years, and currently about 800,000 Americans live in some type of assisted living setting.

Ideally, assisted living allows persons who can no longer live by themselves, but who do not need 24-hour-a-day care, to receive help with daily routines in a homelike setting while supposedly encouraging maximum independence. Residences are generally private rentals, varying in size from one-room efficiencies to full apartments in structures ranging from converted homes to high-rise apartment complexes. Depending on the facility, amenities may include housekeeping, 24-hour security and staff availability, emergency call buttons in each unit, daily room checks, specially prepared foods, three meals a day served in a common dining room, laundry service, transportation, and even social and recreational activities and exercise programs.

On-site nursing services and assistance with activities of daily living—such as bathing, dressing, walking, medication reminders, and meals—are based on an individual's needs. In some facilities the basic fee covers all services. In others, the basic fee covers only limited services with additional charges for services on an as-needed basis. This may partly account for the wide range in daily rates, which vary, approximately, from $15 to $200 nationwide. It is important, therefore, when comparing assisted living arrangements, to ask what is included in the basic rate and what services are available for extra charges. For example, are the services provided by the facility's employees or through other agencies? If you need additional assistance later on, will you have to move? In many states, residents can be dismissed with 30 days notice when their personal care or medical needs exceed the facility's ability or willingness to provide it.

There are some indications that this approach—a largely untested and unregulated industry—is running into problems. Developers reportedly overestimated demand for these centers and have overbuilt. Occupancy rates have leveled off, and operators are under pressure to cut costs and attract new occupants. This makes it especially important to check the financial condition of any facility before signing a contract.

The lack of uniform standards forces consumers shopping for assisted living to rely primarily on providers for information. Be aware that assisted living facilities are often marketed more like real estate than health care. Eldercare Locator, a national toll-free public service of the U.S. Administration on Aging, will provide the phone number of your local aging services agency, which can tell you if any complaints have been filed and whether they have been resolved. You can reach this service at 1-800-677-1116 or get the same information from www.eldercare.gov.

For more information about assisted living, including how to choose a facility, contact the Assisted Living Federation of America, 10300 Eaton Place, Suite 400, Fairfax, VA 22030. Tel: (703) 691-8100; www.alfa.org. Also, contact the Consumer Consortium on Assisted Living, 2342 Oak Street, Falls Church, VA 22046. Tel: (703) 533-8121; www.ccal.org.

Continuing Care Retirement Communities

Continuing care contracts, sometimes called life care contracts, are offered by more than 1,100 continuing care retirement communities (CCRCs) throughout the United States. These communities provide access to a continuum of care and living arrangements on one campus, from apartments or homes for independent seniors to assisted living and nursing facilities. Most people choose to move in when they are still healthy; the average age at entrance is about 75 years. Accommodations vary widely—from luxury suites or bungalows to modest studios—as do the communities' related amenities. Some have auditoriums, tennis courts and swimming pools, elaborate recreation centers, libraries, shopping facilities, movie theaters, and the like on the premises. Often, planned outings and other activities are an integral part of CCRC life. Those who are able may still travel and enjoy life outside the community.

CCRCs promise to provide whatever care you may require throughout your life in a setting appropriate for that level of assistance, and both you and your spouse can live without worrying about "what comes next." You know what facilities you will occupy if you become unable to manage for yourselves. If it becomes necessary, the staff may prepare meals (available for home delivery or in a common dining room), provide housekeeping services and emergency help, and offer custodial or nursing care on a regular basis while you continue to live in an independent setting. And you have the comfort and convenience of living "together" in the community even though one spouse may require full-time nursing care; nursing facilities usually are available on the premises and the non-institutionalized spouse may remain in the apartment. Often, nursing care arrangements proceed flexibly, for example, with daily or weekend visits "home." Or if the need for nursing care ceases, say, after convalescence from surgery, the patient simply returns to his or her apartment (unless the institutionalization of a surviving spouse is terminal).

CCRCs probably are not for everyone. Even though they permit independent living for as long as possible, most such communities cannot avoid an "institutional atmosphere." To some extent, this is intentional—and may be in the interest of most residents. Although residents are free to do as they wish, they are encouraged to participate in community activities as a means of enriching their lives. For many older people, this is a desirable feature, while for others it may not be.

115

Not surprisingly, CCRCs are relatively expensive. Generally, they require a one-time entrance fee and monthly payments thereafter. (In some cases, residents purchase a condominium or cooperative unit instead of paying an initial fee.) Entrance fees vary from lows of $20,000 to highs of $400,000 depending on the CCRC and on the type of living unit, which can range from a studio or "alcove" apartment (one room with scaled-down kitchen and bath) to luxury two-bedroom suites, cluster homes, and even single-family homes.

You usually pay the entrance fee in a lump sum when you sign the continuing care contract, which is the legal agreement that secures your accommodations and services over the long term. Refund policies vary by community and by when you leave (before the contract expires, on death, or after the contract ends). Some communities pay full refunds, while others treat the entrance fee as a nonrefundable "gift;" some refund a percentage of the fees (up to 90 percent) regardless of when or how you leave, while others decrease the refund the longer you stay.

In addition to the entrance fee, current residents can expect to pay from about $450 per month for a low cost CCRC in Oklahoma to about $4,000 per month for a high-cost community in California, or around $5,000 to $50,000 per year in monthly maintenance charges. For most residents, monthly fees fall between these extremes—from $1,250 to $2,500, or between $15,000 and $30,000 per year. In addition, residents must have Medicare and pay for supplemental insurance coverage since CCRCs do not pay for medical bills.

Both the entrance fee and the monthly maintenance fee will vary depending on the type of contract you sign. The more services the contract covers, the more costly it will be. Continuing care contracts generally fall into one of the three categories described below.

All-Inclusive Plans provide, as needed, all the services offered by the CCRC. *Residential services* usually include apartment cleaning and maintenance, dining room service, flat linen laundry service, grounds maintenance, kitchen appliances, personal laundry facilities, dietetic services, use of scheduled transportation, storage, tray service, and utilities. *Health-related services* usually include an emergency call system, home health care in your apartment, long-term nursing care, recreational therapy, and social services. With these plans, your total costs are predictable—but only if the contract pro-

116

hibits or limits inflation adjustments.

Modified Plans usually provide some of the residential services listed above and require an additional fee for other services. They also provide only a *specified amount* of long-term nursing care. If you exceed that amount, you pay an additional charge. Home health care usually is not included in modified plans and additional fees are charged for it.

Fee-for-Service Plans generally provide an independent living unit, limited residential services, and guarantees *access to* nursing care. They do not, however, pay for nursing care; residents must pay full per diem charges, when required.

What You See Now May Not Be What You Get Later

Will the community you committed your bank account and life to be there when you most need it? Perhaps the greatest difficulty with CCRCs is that, in the broadest sense, you may have little flexibility to alter arrangements once you have moved in. Few people want or, if they have poured most of their funds into a CCRC, are able to change residences late in life. For many people, once they have committed funds to a facility, they share its fate. If its financial health fades and the food service starts serving "mystery meals" seven days a week, the attendants become less-attentive than when you first entered the community, or the buildings and grounds, security arrangements, etc. deteriorate, you may be stuck, depending on your contract and circumstances. This situation differs from services that you purchase independently. Those you can change if they are not doing a satisfactory job.

Any CCRC facility's greatest costs are apt to occur when the residential population matures and requires more services. Thus it may not be prudent to enter a "new" community with a large population of relatively young healthy adults—no matter how appealing it may be now. It is this type of facility that is least tested, and could deteriorate dramatically as the fit become unfit. In this respect, the safest facility (in terms of the quality of services it is like to provide in the future) is one that has a "mature" population. If the facility is handling the needs of those people well, and its finances remain sound, then it probably is a good bet.

Thus, if you think a CCRC may be right type of place for you, it pays to shop around. The best way to determine if a facility is well-managed is to visit it. Talk to the residents. Are they satisfied with the services? Is the food good? Has there been any deterioration in the physical facilities or in the "extras"? Most important, obtain copies of the organization's financial statements and review them with your accountant. If they are unsatisfactory or leave unanswered questions, look elsewhere. Finally, buy only a contract that offers a substantial refund at *any* time during its life.

If you are interested in learning more about CCRCs, you should obtain a number of separate publications. Most state insurance departments, listed in Chapter VIII, have published free guides to these facilities. Other useful publications are *The Continuing Care Retirement Community: A Guidebook for Consumers* and the *Consumers' Directory of Continuing Care Retirement Communities,* both available from the American Association of Homes and Services for the Aging (AAHSA), 2519 Connecticut Avenue NW, Washington, D.C. 20008-1520; phone 202-783-2242; www.aahsa.org. The Continuing Care Accreditation Commission establishes standards for CCRC quality and provides consumers with information and a list of accredited communities. For more information, contact the commission at 2519 Connecticut Avenue NW, Washington, D.C. 20008-1520; phone 202-783-7286; www.ccaconline.org.

After you have determined the costs and living conditions of a number of retirement communities, you will be in a better position to compare these with the costs and services that might be obtained elsewhere and that would permit you and your spouse to continue to live in a non-institutional setting—namely, your own home. **In any event, if you think a CCRC may be right for you, start looking early. The waiting lists for entrance into the most desirable communities may be years rather than months.**

Home Health and Elder Care

Presumably, most of us would prefer to remain at home even though we may require assistance of some form—housekeeping services, personal services, health care, or whatever. In fact, many of the services that are provided by nursing homes now are available on a home-care basis from independent contractors and a variety of community and religious groups. Some services are covered by Medicare or Medicaid and many operate on a nonprofit basis or are subsi-

118

dized by local agencies for the aging. Some are provided free of charge.

Home health care services include skilled nursing care, custodial nursing care, home therapy, and clinical testing services (*e.g.*, routine blood tests can be performed by a health care technician in your own home, saving a trip to the doctor's office or clinic). Many local elder care agencies provide low cost or free transportation for senior citizens, volunteer housekeeping services, live-in companion referrals, "meals on wheels" food services, shopping services, and the like.

Also, families caring for loved ones can get rest and time off through services such as adult day care and respite care. And today, so-called life-call communications services are widely available to homebound seniors for a relatively modest fee, providing help at the press of a button in case of a personal or medical emergency.

Your Own "Life-Care" Home?

Especially in view of the Medicaid exemption of assets held in the home, it may be possible for many elderly persons to create their own "life-care" home by altering the structure of their house to accommodate walkers or wheelchairs or by adding a "companion's quarters" and utilizing the many home-health and elder care services now available. Of course, this requires planning ahead and major expenditures. But if a comparison of the costs and benefits of home care with the major alternatives, such as nursing homes and continuing care retirement communities, reveals substantial potential savings, you may be better off to consider a home-care plan of your own design.

There are thousands of elder care services in localities across the United States. Your local Yellow Pages may contain listings under "Home Health Services" and "Senior Citizens' Service Organizations" that can direct you to local care providers. The accompanying "Directory of State Agencies on Aging" lists offices that can provide you with further information. In addition to the offices listed there, you can find the location and telephone number of the nearest state and local agencies for the aging by calling Eldercare Locator, a toll-free information service funded by the Federal government. Their toll-free telephone number is 1-800-677-1116 and their website is www.eldercare.gov. They have information on over 4,800 state and local agencies and organizations. Information is also available from the Federal Administration on Aging, 330 Independence Ave., SW, Washington, DC 20201; 202-619-7501; www.aoa.dhhs.gov.

DIRECTORY OF STATE AGENCIES ON AGING

Alabama

Department of Senior Services .... (334) 242-5743
770 Washington Ave., Suite 470, P. O. Box 301851, Montgomery, AL 36130-1851

Alaska

Commission on Aging .... (907) 465-4879
P. O. Box 110209, Juneau, AK 99811-0209

Arizona

Aging and Adult Administration .... (602) 542-4446
1789 W. Jefferson St., #950A, Phoenix, AZ 85007

Arkansas

Division of Aging and Adult Services .... (501) 682-2441
1417 Donaghey Plaza South, P. O. Box 1437/Slot S-530, Little Rock, AR 72203-1437

California

Department of Aging .... (916) 322-5290
1600 K St., Sacramento, CA 95814

Colorado

Aging & Adult Services .... (303) 866-2636
1575 Sherman St., Ground Floor, Denver CO 80203

Connecticut

Division of Elderly Services .... (860) 424-5277
25 Sigourney St., 10th Floor, Hartford CT 06106-5033

Delaware

Services for Aging .... (302) 577-4791
Dept. of Health & Social Services, 1901 N. DuPont Hwy., New Castle, DE 19720

District of Columbia

Office on Aging .... (202) 724-5622
One Judiciary Square, 441 4th St., N.W., 9th Fl., Washington, D.C. 20001

Florida

Department of Elder Affairs .... (850) 414-2000
4040 Esplanade Way, Bldg. B, Suite 152, Tallahassee, FL 32399

Georgia

Division of Aging Services .... (404) 657-5258
Dept. of Human Resources, 2 Peachtree St., N.E. 9th Floor Atlanta GA 30303

Hawaii

Executive Office on Aging .... (808) 586-0100
250 S. Hotel St., Suite 109, 4th Floor, Honolulu, HI 96813-2381

Idaho

Commission on Aging .... (208) 334-3833
3880 Americana Terr., Ste.120, Boise, ID 83720

Illinois

Department on Aging .... (217) 785-2870
421 E. Capitol Ave., Springfield, IL 62701

Indiana

Bureau of Aging and In-Home Services .... (317) 232-7020
402 W. Washington St., P. O. Box 7083, Indianapolis, IN
46207-7083

Iowa

Department of Elder Affairs .... (515) 242-3333
200 10th St., 3rd Fl., Des Moines, IA 50309-3609

Kansas

Department on Aging .... (785) 296-5222
503 S. Kansas Ave., New England Bldg., Topeka, KS 66603-
3404

Kentucky

Office of Aging Services .... (502) 564-6930
Cabinet for Familes & Children, 275 E. Main St., Frankfort,
KY 40621

Louisiana

Governor's Office of Elderly Affairs .... (225) 342-7100
4550 N. Boulevard, 2nd Fl., P. O. Box 80374, Baton Rouge,
LA 70898-0374

Maine

Bureau of Elder & Adult Services .... (207) 624-5335
35 Anthony Ave., State House Station #11, Augusta, ME
04333

Maryland

Department of Aging .... (410) 767-1100
301 W. Preston St., Room 1007, Baltimore, MD 21201

Massachusetts

Executive Office of Elder Affairs .... (617) 222-7451
One Ashburton Place, 5th Fl., Boston, MA 02108

Michigan

Office of Services to the Aging .... (517) 373-8230
7109 West Saginaw, P. O. Box 30676, Lansing, MI 48909

Minnesota

Board on Aging .... (651) 296-2770
Human Services Bldg., 444 Lafayette Road, St. Paul,
MN 55155-3843

Mississippi

Division of Aging & Adult Services .... (601) 359-4925
750 North State St., Jackson, MS 39202

Missouri

Division of Senior Services .... (573) 751-3082
615 Howertan Court, Jefferson City, MO 65102

Montana

Senior & Long Term Care Division .... (406) 444-4077
111 North Sanders, P.O. Box 4210, Helena, MT 59620

Nebraska

Division on Aging .... (402) 471-2307
301 Centennial Mall-South, P.O. Box 95044, Lincoln, NE 68509

Nevada

Division for Aging Services .... (775) 687-4210
Dept. of Human Resources, 3416 Goni Rd., Bldg. D-132, Carson City, NV 89706

New Hampshire

Division of Elderly & Adult Services .... (603) 271-4680
Dept. of Health & Human Services, State Office Park South, 129 Pleasant St., Bldg.. #1, Concord, NH 03301

New Jersey

Division of Senior Affairs .... (609) 943-3345
Dept. of Health & Human Services, P.O. Box 807, Trenton, NJ 08625-0807

New Mexico

State Agency on Aging .... (505) 827-7640
La Villa Rivera Bldg., 228 E. Palace Ave., Santa Fe, NM 87501

New York

State Office for the Aging .... (518) 474-7012
2 Empire State Plaza, Albany, NY 12223-1251

North Carolina

Division of Aging .... (919) 733-3983
2101 Mail Serv. Ctr., Raleigh, NC 27699-2101

North Dakota

Aging Services Division .... (701) 328-4601
Dept. of Human Services, 600 South 2nd St., Ste. 1C, Bismarck, ND 58504

Ohio

Department of Aging .... (614) 466-5500
50 West Broad St., 9th Fl., Columbus, OH 43215-5928

Oklahoma

Aging Services Division .... (405) 521-2327
Dept. of Human Services, 312 NE 28th St., Oklahoma City, OK 73125

Oregon

Seniors & People with Disabilities .... (503) 945-5811
500 Summer St., NE, Salem, OR 97310-1073

Pennsylvania

Department of Aging .... (717) 783-1550
Commonwealth of Pennsylvania, Forum Place, 555 Walnut, 5th Floor, Harrisburg, PA 17101-1919

Puerto Rico

Governor's Office of Elderly Affairs ...... (787) 721-5710
P.O. Box 50063, Old San Juan Station, PR 00902

Rhode Island

Department of Elderly Affairs .... (401) 462-3000
35 Howard Ave., Cranston RI 02920

South Carolina

Senior and Long Term Care Services .... (803) 898-2501
P.O. Box 8206, Columbia, SC 29202-8206

South Dakota

Office of Adult Services and Aging .... (605) 773-3656
700 Governor's Drive, Richard F. Kneip Bldg., Pierre, SD 57501-2291

Tennessee

Commission on Aging & Disability .... (615) 741-2056
Andrew Jackson Bldg., 9th Fl., 500 Deadrick St., Nashville, TN 37243-0860

Texas

Department of Aging .... (512) 424-6840
4900 North Lamar, 4th Fl., Austin, TX 78751-2316

Utah

Division of Aging and Adult Services .... (801) 539-3910
120 North 200 West, P.O. Box 45500, Salt Lake City, UT 84145-0500

Vermont

Department of Aging & Disabilities .... (802) 241-2400
Waterbury Complex, 103 S. Main St., Waterbury, VT 05671-2301

Virginia

Department for the Aging .... (804) 662-9333
1600 Forest, Ste. 102, Richmond, VA 23229

Washington

Aging & Adult Services Administration .... (360) 725-2310
Dept. of Social & Health Services, P. O. Box 45050, Olympia, WA 98504-5050

West Virginia

Bureau of Senior Citizens .... (304) 558-3317
Holly Grove- Bldg. 10, 1900 Kanawha Blvd. E., Charleston, WV 25305

Wisconsin

Department of Health & Family Services ..... (608) 266-2536
1 West Wilson St., Rm 450, Madison, WI 53707-7850

Wyoming

Division on Aging .... (307) 777-7986
6101 Yellowstone Rd., Suite 259B, Cheyenne, WY 82002-0710

XII.
MEDICAID: A MIDDLE-CLASS FINANCIAL OPTION?

THE 1989 repeal of the Medicare Catastrophic Coverage Act opened the door to vastly increased enrollment of otherwise "middle-class" beneficiaries in the Federal-State co-sponsored Medicaid programs originally intended to provide care for only the neediest patients. Amendments to the Medicaid laws in the 1990s complicated this somewhat by changing rules and criminalizing some activities, but middle-class use of Medicaid for long-term care is not likely to be significantly reduced.

Medicaid plays a substantial role in financing long-term care. The program pays for an average of 46 percent of all care provided in nursing homes and by home health services. In 1998 Medicaid payments for custodial nursing care and home health care totaled roughly $35 billion for the more than 2.8 million recipients of these services—an average expenditure of about $12,500 per long-term recipient. Only 11 percent of Medicaid beneficiaries are elderly, but because their care is expensive, they account for 31 percent of costs. Not surprisingly, then, with an aging population, long-term care payments play an increasingly larger role in total Medicaid spending and are already the program's largest single cost.

Overall, Medicaid costs have grown by about 13 percent annually in recent years. The rising costs of health care and prescription drugs, the weak economic recovery, and broadened eligibility requirements may all be factors in this growth. Medicaid accounts for the largest expenditure in state budgets next to education (an average of 20 percent). Not surprisingly, states are contemplating new restrictions on eligibility and benefits to reduce the strain on already tight budgets.

Lobbyists for the elderly have long insisted that the potential costs of long-term nursing or custodial care pose the single largest potential financial risk to most retirees of average means. Indeed, the costs of a year's stay in a nursing home now average from $30,000 to $65,000 nationwide (in some states, such as New York, the cost can be much higher.) The savings of over two-thirds of current nursing home residents are totally depleted within 24 months of their admission. Elder advocates have publicized such data and vigorously lobbied for Medicare coverage for long-term custodial care to no avail. Understandably, many retirees are concerned that nursing home costs could quickly wipe them out. In fact, only a relatively small proportion of the elderly face lengthy confinement in a nursing home. Even so, fear of nursing home costs has spawned a new area of financial planning, as described below.

The 1989 Medicare legislation that repealed the Catastrophic Coverage Act also rescinded most of the prohibitions against so-called Medicaid trusts, which permit retirees to become eligible for Medicaid's nursing home coverage without dissipating their estates. The law also provided at-home spouses of institutionalized Medicaid patients with substantial protection against impoverishment. The apparent result has been a proliferation both of attorneys who specialize in drafting Medicaid trusts that meet the technical requirements of the law and of middle-class clients who want their wealth sheltered in the event they need long-term care.

Reportedly, the liberalized treatment of trust arrangements designed to promote Medicaid eligibility was a "compromise" intended to offset in part the effects of the repeal of Medicare's catastrophic coverage provisions and to provide some relief for those forced to enter nursing homes. From the perspective of Washington lawmakers, it also achieved another goal. Unlike Medicare, which is Federally-funded, a substantial portion of Medicaid costs are funded by *state* taxes. In effect, by limiting Medicare catastrophic illness and long-term care coverage while relaxing middle-class prohibitions on Medicaid eligibility, Congress shifted a portion of the costs of such programs onto the states.

The liberalization of Medicaid eligibility has been somewhat reversed over the past decade. Amendments in 1993 to the Medicaid law required states to remove the cap on the penalty for transferring assets at less than market value for the purpose of becoming eligible for Medicaid. The penalty is calculated by dividing the value of the transferred assets by the average monthly private pay rate for nursing facilities in the particular state. The result is the number of months of Medicaid ineligibility. The 1989 legislation had capped this period of ineligibility at 30 months; the 1993 legislation removed the cap. The law also required states to increase the "lookback" period over which they can check for such transfers of assets,

126

to three years for transfers to individuals and to five years for transfers to certain types of trusts.

The Health Insurance Portability and Accountability Act (1996), also known as the Kassebaum-Kennedy health reform bill, made asset transfers to qualify for Medicaid for nursing home or other long-term care a federal crime in addition to already being subject to the penalties described above. This provision passed with no hearings and no debate. Not one House member claimed authorship. The provision, dubbed the "Granny Goes to Jail Law," was poorly drafted and unclear on many issues, such as who might be prosecuted and whether the crime involved was a felony or misdemeanor.

The Balanced Budget Act of 1997 amended this provision to read that the criminal penalties of the "Granny" provision applied only to those who "for a fee counsel or assist an individual to make certain transfers of assets" for the purpose of qualifying for Medicaid. This law, dubbed the "Granny's Lawyer Goes to Jail Law," came under immediate fire. In 1998, U.S. Attorney General Janet Reno stated that she would not enforce the law. Later, the New York State Bar Association challenged the law's constitutionality and won a nationwide injunction against its enforcement. The Justice Department filed a notice of appeal that was ultimately withdrawn.

Ironically, the current law may not discourage asset shifting, but rather may encourage more and earlier transfers. The longer lookback periods, three years for transfers to individuals and five years for transfers to trusts, may also encourage relatively more transfers to individuals rather than to trusts. One issue that few people seem to consider, however, is that a significant proportion of nursing home residents recover from the conditions that led to their confinement and go home again. If these people have intentionally impoverished themselves to qualify for Medicaid, they may now be unable to support themselves or find themselves at the mercy of the beneficiaries of their transferred wealth.

In any event, you should not apply for Medicaid until at least three years after you make any transfers to individuals and five years after transfers to some trusts. Application during these lookback periods may result in penalties and possible criminal action against paid advisers. This area of legislation could change frequently over the next few years. For example, some states are now asking the

Federal government for permission to extend the look-back period on transfers to individuals to as long as six years. For current information on Medicaid and other legal issues for elders, contact the National Senior Citizens Law Center, 1101 14th Street NW, Suite 400, Washington, DC 20005; phone (202) 289-6976; website www.nsclc.org.

Comprehensive Medicaid Coverage

Medicaid coverage for medical services varies markedly (in amount, duration, and scope) from state to state, within the range of Federal Medicaid standards. All states are required to provide "core" coverage for a variety of services, including inpatient and outpatient hospital services, laboratory and x-ray services, skilled nursing facility services, physicians' and some dentists' services, home health care, medical supplies and appliances, physical and occupational therapy, and speech pathology and audiology services. In addition, all states must pay the transportation costs of Medicaid recipients for travel to and from their health care providers. Many states also include coverage for services of chiropractors, optometrists, podiatrists, private nurses, dental care (including dentures), eyeglasses, and prescription drugs.

Even Medicaid's "·ore" coverage is substantially greater than that offered to Medicare subscribers or to holders even of the costliest Medicare supplemental insurance policies. In most states, Medicaid beneficiaries receive virtually all medical goods and services, even peripheral ones, free of charge. Most pertinent for this discussion, Medicaid pays for the costs of *custodial* nursing home care once certain income and asset criteria are met.

From a clinical perspective, Medicaid's chief drawback is that not all physicians and health care institutions will take Medicaid cases. Especially in the case of nursing home care, the better-rated care facilities may not accept Medicaid patients. Thus, many impoverished Medicaid recipients have been forced to accept treatment at substandard "Medicaid clinics" and have ended up at "Medicaid mill" nursing homes. However, in the case of middle-class retirees whose financial plans include the deliberate transfer of assets and "spend downs" to qualify for Medicaid coverage, nursing home admission can be made on a private-payment basis and the "cold-shoulder" treatment usually reserved for destitute Medicaid patients

128

avoided.

Medicaid Eligibility Requirements

Each state determines its own Medicaid eligibility requirements within broad Federal guidelines. Policies are complex and vary considerably from state to state; *e.g.*, a person eligible for Medicaid in one state may not be eligible in another. Furthermore, rules governing both eligibility and services can change during the year in any state.

Generally, states are required to provide Medicaid services to most recipients of Federal and/or state income assistance or related programs. Recipients who in most states automatically qualify for Medicaid include those receiving Aid to Families with Dependent Children (AFDC), Supplemental Security Income (SSI), and certain Medicare beneficiaries (discussed below). States may also provide Medicaid coverage for a variety of "categorically needy" groups, including infants and pregnant women whose family income is at or below 185 percent of the Federal poverty level; aged, blind, or disabled adults whose incomes and assets may be above the SSI threshold but below the Federal poverty level; institutionalized persons with income and resources below specified limits; and "medically needy" persons.

Some aged, blind, and disabled persons are covered under both Medicare and Medicaid as "dual beneficiaries" whose Medicare Part B premiums and Medicare coinsurance are paid by Medicaid. Dual beneficiaries also receive some, but not all, of the more-comprehensive Medicaid coverage described above, including eyeglasses and hearing aids. Such "qualified Medicare beneficiaries" are individuals with incomes at or below the Federal poverty level and resources at or below twice the standard allowed under the SSI program. Based on those criteria, Medicare beneficiaries 65 years or over become eligible for Medicaid in 2003 when "countable" income falls below $9,228 per year for a single individual and $12,360 for a couple and "countable" assets do not exceed $4,000 for an individual.

Not all income is included in "countable" income and certain assets are exempt from the inventory of resources. For example, a spouse confined to a nursing home in 2004 may deduct from monthly income at least $30 for personal needs, a $1,515 to $2,319 monthly allowance for the at-home spouse, and an allowance for each additional family member of at least one-third of the allowance for the at-home spouse. An individual's or couple's home, automobile (up to a certain value), household goods and personal effects of "reasonable" value, and burial plots and life insurance with a face value up to $1,500 or burial funds up to $1,500 are exempt assets. The "spousal impoverishment protection" provisions of the 1989 repeal of the Medicare Catastrophic Coverage Act entitle the at-home spouse to retain, in 2004, a minimum of $18,552, or one-half of the couple's total resources up to a maximum of $92,760. Moreover, if one spouse must enter a nursing home, the law protects exempt assets (car, household goods, and personal effects) to *any* value, even if it is much higher than SSI limits.

In short, current legislation provides liberal exemptions of both income and assets from Medicaid eligibility tests. Today, many of the middle-class aged may qualify for Medicaid and still retain substantial income and resources, especially if a couple's liquid assets (bank accounts, CDs, stocks, bonds) are converted into exempt assets and a portion of them—sufficient to produce income up to the Medicaid limits—annuitized.

Asset Conversion

For couples with liquid assets under $350,000 or so, the least involved and least costly way to protect financial resources from Medicaid "spend down" requirements is to convert them to exempt-category assets. For example, all outstanding debt should be paid at once. If a couple's home has a mortgage, nonexempt assets held in savings accounts, stocks, and bonds can be used to pay off the outstanding mortgage balance, which immediately converts those funds to an exempt category, the home. If the couple rents but has substantial savings, the savings can be used to purchase a condominium home that will be exempt. Or if the family car needs replacing, nonexempt resources could be used to purchase a new one, which would be exempt under the spousal impoverishment protection legislation.

Similarly, liquid assets can be used to make home improvements or to purchase household goods that are exempt from Medicaid resource limitations. Preventive and cost-saving home repairs can be made that would be prohibitively expensive under Medicaid's income limitations. These could include a new roof, siding, windows, plumbing and heating, wiring, insulation, or energy-efficient labor saving appliances that reduce living costs for the at-home spouse. Even major remodeling (such as a new kitchen or bathrooms), additions to the structure, or low-maintenance landscaping might be contemplated as a means of protecting assets at the same time they "make life easier" for the spouse at home.

And by annuitizing remaining liquid assets, a portion of otherwise "countable" financial resources can be converted into largely, perhaps totally, exempt income. At current annuity rates, a $100,000 lifetime annuity purchased at age 65 would yield an income of about $7,200 per year to an at-home female spouse—$8,500 per year if she were 75.

Pouring assets into the family home provides "ironclad" protection only so long as the at-home spouse or certain other relations reside there. After that spouse or other relations vacate the residence or die, the state may (but is not required to) seek "recovery" of Medicaid outlays for nursing home expenses after the death of the institutionalized beneficiary—unless the property has been transferred outright to another party, such as the heirs.

Never attempt asset conversion for the purpose of meeting Medicaid eligibility without first consulting an attorney and accountant who specialize in this area and are familiar with the laws in your state. Of course, the establishment of a Medicaid trust, described next, will also require professional counsel.

Medicaid Trusts

If total "countable" assets exceed Medicaid limits even after the above measures have been taken, they can still be sheltered using so-called "Medicaid trusts." In brief, within certain "look-back" periods Medicaid law does not permit individuals to transfer assets to individuals or to a trust in order to qualify under Medicaid's income and resource limits. Federal law requires that states "look back" at least three years for transfers of assets to individuals (and some trusts) and at least five years for transfers of assets to certain trusts. Once the look-back period ends, however, the grantor can become eligible for Medicaid coverage.

Medicaid trusts have become a big business. Reportedly, "elder-

131

practice" law firms in the larger metropolitan areas regularly host Medicaid trust promotions for senior citizen audiences, hoping to drum up clients. For legal fees of around $2,500 or $3,500, such firms will draft a trust agreement that meets Medicaid qualifications.

Medicaid trusts usually are "conventional" irrevocable trust agreements with special provisions added to satisfy the needs of long-term care patients and the requirements of the Medicaid authorities. Although each agreement is different depending on individual circumstances, Medicaid trusts generally have two common characteristics: (1) they require that income from the trust, or trust principal as required, be used to pay the costs of long-term nursing care during periods of ineligibility, and (2) they are designed so that "countable" income from the trust, including "outside" buildup, does not exceed Medicaid limits. (Thus, trust assets could be limited to low-income or no-income holdings.) Such provisions could be made through a "springing trust" arrangement in which a *revocable* trust agreement, which retains complete control of trust assets until the last minute, would automatically become an *irrevocable* Medicaid trust when the grantor enters a nursing home. Because the Medicaid laws are subject to change at either the Federal or the state level, trust agreements may need to be modified periodically to conform to the latest legal requirements.

A Public-Private Medicaid "Partnership"?

The increased use of Medicaid by the middle class has prompted officials in some states to look for ways to reduce the consequent financial strain on state budgets. The public-private "partnership program" mentioned in Chapter X is one such "experiment." It provides incentives for elderly persons to purchase private long-term care insurance in return for the state's promise to waive Medicaid eligibility spend-down requirements for nursing home costs when private insurance benefits cease. Under the program, participants generally can qualify for Medicaid based only on their income; the asset test that is normally applied to Medicaid applicants is waived.

Called the "Partnership for Long-Term Care," the program was developed under a grant from the Robert Wood Johnson Foundation Program to Promote Long-Term Care Insurance for the Elderly. Four states—California, Connecticut, Indiana, and New York—currently participate.

132

The New York plan clearly states that the desired market is primarily the middle-class elderly – single persons with a total income of at least $30,000 per year and assets of at least $60,000 (excluding a home) and married persons with yearly incomes between $40,000 and $50,000 and assets over $140,000.

According to the New York plan, individuals who participate must purchase and maintain in force an approved private long-term care policy that promises to pay benefits for nursing home care for three years, for home care for six years, or for an equivalent combination of both. In return, New York will disregard assets (but not income) when determining Medicaid eligibility. In other words, there is no limit to the assets you may keep and still qualify for Medicaid, as long as your income is sufficiently low.

Efforts to expand the Partnership program into other states have been blocked since 1993 by restrictions enacted by Congress. These restrictions require states operating such programs to recover Medicaid costs from the estates of all persons receiving services under Medicaid. Thus, the beneficiary's assets are protected only while he is alive. After his death Medicaid will "go after" assets left in the estate to help reimburse the government for its costs of care. The four states that currently offer Partnership programs created them before 1993 and were exempted from this law.

Interested persons residing in the four participating states can write to the Partnership for Long-Term Care, National Program Office, University of Maryland Center of Aging, 1240 HHP Building, College Park, MD 20742-2611; call 301-405-7555; or visit the program's website at www.hhp.umd.edu/AGING/. There are also websites for each state program: California (www.dhs.ca.gov/cpltc), Connecticut (www.CTpartnership.org), Indiana (www.IN.gov/fssa/iltcp) and New York (www.nyspltc.org).

Must We All Become Thieves?

Of course, Medicaid never was intended to be a financial tool of the middle class. It was designed to provide medical relief to the genuinely needy. Almost surely, some middle-class retirees who would *never* steal from their neighbors but *have* taken advantage of Medicaid trusts are uncomfortable with the notion that in their efforts to prevent the dissipation of their own wealth they have gone on the dole at the expense of other taxpayers. In this respect, a number of commentators who usually favor social legislation have observed that middle-class "abuse" of Medicaid threatens to bankrupt the program.

Others, including the attorneys who profit therefrom, defend the use of Medicaid trusts as a legal means to preserve one's hard-earned wealth that in practical effect is no different from tax shelters, which permit some to pay less tax than others who deploy their assets in less-advantaged ways. Still others argue that by entering the Medicaid rolls, they simply are seeking partial restitution for the Government's prior confiscation of their wealth that has funded programs that almost surely will impoverish their children and grandchildren unless their inheritance is preserved.

From a purely ethical standpoint, it may be difficult for most people to distinguish the "right" from the "wrong" in any of these positions. Rather, it would seem that questions of who are the "more deserving" are largely political and are incapable of final resolution. What is more clear is that many no doubt *will* take advantage of all legal means to prevent the dissipation of their wealth. The inexorable result is the tendency to make "suckers" of anyone who does not do likewise, even if he or she is in general sympathy with the original goals of programs such as Medicaid.

This process seems characteristic of almost any regime that seeks, beyond some as-yet unmeasured extent, to advantage some people at the expense of others. Seemingly, those who are disadvantaged eventually seek redress by one means or another, usually by demanding "benefits" for themselves. The result effectively defeats the original intent of the program. For example, Social Security was originally intended to be a "safety net," but has instead become an inefficient public retirement program that has financed Government profligacy and fostered one of the most massive transfers of wealth in history (from one generation to another). Such programs also can be harmful in other ways, notably in the loss of self-reliance they encourage and the related "command" regimes they spawn. Perhaps most serious, they tend to corrupt human relations and beget social pathology. As in the case of Medicaid, they threaten to make thieves of us all.

Part 4
END-OF-LIFE DECISIONS

XIII.
LEGAL CONSIDERATIONS

OF great concern to many older people is the possibility that if they become irreversibly ill and are unable to make decisions for themselves, artificial means will be used to prolong their lives long after they have any hope of recovery and long after they would wish to remain "alive," were they able to speak for themselves. Not only does such treatment often prolong the anguish of family and friends, but it also can be financially devastating to the survivors who may be forced to pay the costs of such care.

In today's litigious society, however, virtually no care provider—hospital, nursing home, or physician—is willing to accept the potential liability for withholding life-prolonging care. This is so even when a patient's life is being sustained under highly artificial circumstances and where there is no hope of recovery.

The only way to ensure that your wishes are carried out is to state your instructions in writing according to the procedures required by the pertinent laws of the state in which you reside.

Living Wills

Most states now have a "living will" statute. Even in states without such a statute, living wills may be recognized in practice. A living will allows you to declare your wishes with respect to the kind of medical treatment you wish to receive in the event you become unable to make your own decisions. It may or may not appoint a person to make medical decisions on your behalf. For that, you may need to use a separate form (discussed in the next section) that assigns "durable power of attorney for health care" to a person you appoint as your "health care agent."

A living will serves as a guide for your health care agent or anyone else, such as doctors and family members, who may be making decisions about your treatment. Even if you think your family "knows" what you would want done if you become incapacitated, a living will provides a written record of your preferences. This is valuable from both a legal perspective and, for loved ones making difficult decisions, a personal perspective.

In some states it is not necessary to have a lawyer draw up a living will. However, you must use the form that has been approved for use in your state. To obtain a copy of a living will form for your state, see your attorney or contact Last Acts Partnership (formerly Choices in Dying, which created the first living will). This national nonprofit organization provides the information, instructions, and forms you need to ensure that your preferences are followed at the end of life. Its "Tending to the Ending Kit" ($10) includes a complete set of "advance directives" (legal documents) and instructions for your state. The Partnership also publishes a useful book, *Advance Directives and End-of-Life Decisions* ($5.95). Contact Last Acts Partnership, 1620 Eye Street NW, Suite 202, Washington DC 20006; 1-800-989-WILL (1-800-989-9455); or www.lastactspartnership.org.

After completing a state-specific advance directive package, you should always speak to your doctors about your wishes. They can also provide you with any additional form they may require in order to honor your instructions.

All living wills must be signed and witnessed, and it is prudent (and may be required by law) to have such documents notarized as well. Witnesses to a living will should not be anyone who would "benefit" from your death through an inheritance or otherwise. Usually the following individuals are specifically prohibited by statute from witnessing a living will: anyone related to the declarant by blood or marriage; any heir or claimant to any part of the declarant's estate, including creditors; the declarant's physician or physician's employee; any employee of the patient's health facility; or any other person responsible for the patient's health care.

Once the living will is prepared, you should keep the original with your personal papers. You should give copies to your doctors, members of your family, and your health care agent. Some states require that a living will be updated periodically. Even if your state does not, you should review the living will periodically to make sure that it still accurately states your wishes and initial and date it to so indicate.

In some states the prescribed form must be followed precisely. Other states permit personalized instructions. The contents of the living will in these states will differ for each individual depending on his or her wishes with respect to certain medical circumstances, including "hydration" and "feeding," that *must* be specified in the document. Prescribed forms are not intended to be used as "finished documents," but only as starting points for drafting a living will in consultation with your attorney and other interested parties.

In states that do not have a prescribed form, living will declarations should be drafted to meet the requirements of health care providers and other pertinent law. On page 141 is a sample form that has been widely distributed in those states and may serve as a foundation for a living will declaration (and health care proxy) in consultation with your attorney and health care providers. In some states, such as New Jersey, attorneys have available a lengthy living will form that accommodates that state's relatively lengthy, comprehensive law respecting refusal of life-supporting medical care.

Durable Powers of Attorney for Health Care
(Health Care Proxies)

Many health care analysts advise that a durable power of attorney for health care (health care proxy) should accompany the living will. The specified living will forms in some states include such a health care proxy and should be used when available. In other states the health care proxy is a separate form.

In brief, a durable power of attorney for health care empowers someone of your choosing to act in your behalf should you become unable to communicate or make decisions for yourself. This health care agent will be able to make decisions *only* if you are unable to do so. As long as you have the capacity to make decisions, your consent will be required for medical treatment.

Plainly, you should choose your health care agent carefully and thoroughly discuss with him or her your wishes as expressed in your living will. That probably will require going into specific detail about precise procedures, under precisely which circumstances you do or do not wish them to be used, and, if you choose, for what length of time these procedures should be performed. In most states and the District of Columbia, health care agents are permitted to make medical decisions specifically including decisions to withdraw or withhold life support. However, in other states the force of health care proxies is limited to one degree or another. Nevertheless, if you have a health care proxy that is supported by a properly drafted living will declaration, and you have had the appropriate discussion of your wishes with your agent and your doctors, you are in a strong position to see that your wishes are carried out.

As with living wills, the legal forms for health care proxies vary from state to state. You should use the form that is specified by your state. These forms are available in Last Act Partnership's "Tending to the Ending Kit" and on their web site cited above. A sample health care proxy that may serve as a rough example is printed on page 142. This form should not be used as your living will.

Since the issues may be complex, it is important that individuals determine their wishes with respect to end-of-life medical treatment while they are still able and discuss them with their physician, loved ones, and health care agent. Even the most carefully prepared documents cannot guarantee that your wishes will be carried out. However, if you have not prepared a living will and a health care proxy, it is almost guaranteed that they will *not* be.

Sample Living Will

If I should have an incurable or irreversible condition that will cause my death within a relatively short time, and I am no longer able to make decisions regarding my medical treatment or if I should become permanently unconscious, I direct my attending physician, pursuant to state laws, to withhold or withdraw treatments that only prolong the process of dying and are not necessary to my comfort or to alleviate pain.

With regard to artificially supplied nutrition and hydration, I specifically direct that

(check the option desired):
( ) artificial nutrition be withheld after consultation with my attending physician.
( ) artificial hydration be withheld after consultation with my attending physician.

(check the option desired):
( ) artificial nutrition may *not* be withheld.
( ) artificial hydration may *not* be withheld.

Other directions: _____

I direct my attending physician, pursuant to the state laws, to follow the instructions of

_____
(name of proxy)

whom I appoint as my Health Care Proxy to make medical treatment decisions on my behalf, including whether life-sustaining treatment should be withheld or withdrawn.

Signed this _____ day of _____, _____.
                (day)   *(month)*   *(year)*

Signature_____

The declarant voluntarily signed this writing in my presence

Witness_____

Witness_____

Sample Durable Power of Attorney for Health Care

I, _____, hereby appoint:
(name)

_____
(name, home address and telephone number of agent)

as my health care agent to make any and all health care decisions for me, except to the extent that I state otherwise.

This Durable Power of Attorney for Health Care shall take effect in the event I become unable to make my own health care decisions. My health care agent and any alternate health care agent shall have the authority to make all health care decisions regarding any care, treatment, service, or procedure to maintain, diagnose, treat, or provide for my physical or mental health or personal care. My health care agent and any alternate agent shall also have the authority to make decisions regarding the providing, witholding or withdrawing of life sustaining treatment pursuant to state laws.

Optional Instructions: _____

If the health care agent I appoint is unable, unwilling or unavailable to act as my health care agent, then I appoint:

_____
(name, home address and telephone number of agent)

Signed this _____ day of _____, _____.
               (day)   *(month)*   *(year)*

Signature_____

Statement by Witnesses (must be 18 or older)

I declare that the person who signed this document appeared to execute the durable power of attorney for health care willingly and free from duress. He or she signed (or asked another to sign for him or her) this document in my presence.

Witness_____
                 (Sign and Print name)

Witness_____
                 (Sign and Print name)

XIV.
FUNERAL OPTIONS

DEATH is one of the few events that every human experiences. Nevertheless, the disposition of a person's physical remains often is one of the least-planned of his or her affairs. Fears about death understandably may make all concerned, especially family members, reluctant to discuss or plan funeral arrangements much in advance of actual need. However, "last minute" arrangements made in hastened or anguished circumstances can be far more costly—sometimes onerously so to survivors—than informed decisions reached before death stares one in the face. As a practical matter, the disposition of one's physical remains might prudently be arranged just as one plans for the disposition of one's legal estate.

In this respect there are far more funeral options available than many may realize. For many people, knowing that after they die they will be celebrated by a funeral that spares no expense and is attended by a host of friends and family is an important source of satisfaction during their remaining lifetime. For others, a private funeral of modest proportions that does not pose a financial burden to survivors, or deplete the estate that will pass to heirs, is desirable. Still others prefer that no funeral service be held, and that their remains be disposed of in the least costly fashion. Your own wishes probably will not be fulfilled unless you make them known—and unless you review the options that are available for a particular type of funeral arrangement.

Funeral Regulations

Whatever those wishes may be, a variety of state and Federal laws regulate funeral practice. It is in your interest and the interest of your survivors to be familiar with the principal laws governing the disposition of human remains and funeral industry operations. The Federal Trade Commission's "Funeral Rule" (16 CFR Part 453) enables consumers to obtain information about funeral costs. Among other provisions, the Funeral Rule requires that funeral providers give price information over the telephone (which relieves buyers of funeral services of subtle "pressure" tactics that may be employed in a face-to-face meeting with funeral personnel). It also requires them to supply, on request, a general price list of all items and services offered.

In order to help consumers decide on whether to purchase it, the Funeral Rule also requires that customers be given information about embalming and specifies that funeral providers: 1) must not falsely state that embalming is required by law; 2) must disclose in writing (with some exceptions) when embalming is *not* required by law; 3) may not charge a fee for unauthorized embalming unless it is required by law; 4) disclose in writing that (usually) you have the right to choose between cremation or immediate burial if you do not want embalming; and 5) disclose in writing under what circumstances embalming is a practical necessity.

The Funeral Rule stipulates that funeral providers disclose any fees that they charge for so-called "cash advance" items related to funeral arrangements. These are items or services that the funeral director purchases in your behalf, but that you could purchase yourself, and they include flowers, obituary notices, clergy honoraria, and the like. The Funeral Rule requires that the provider inform you if a fee is added to the price of cash advance items or if the provider gets a "kick back" from any of the suppliers.

One of the most costly items in most funerals is the casket. However, in some circumstances a casket may not be appropriate. For consumers who select direct cremation, for example, an inexpensive alternative container or unfinished wood box that will be destroyed during cremation may suffice. Under the Funeral Rule, funeral directors who offer cremation services are prohibited from telling you that state or local law requires a casket for direct cremations and must make an unfinished wood box or alternative container available.

In short, there are a variety of options available for conventional funerals that could bewilder your survivors. It is not much trouble to telephone one or more funeral providers in your locality, listed under "Funeral Homes" in the Yellow Pages, to request a "general price list" of funeral items and services. Such lists are yours to keep, and you may wish to discuss them with whomever you expect to be in charge of funeral arrangements when the time comes – and to indicate on the price list exactly what you want. A copy of this list, with your written instructions, ought to be kept in a readily available location in the event of your death (but *not* in a safe deposit box), and be made known ahead of time to your spouse or anyone else who may require such information upon your death.

For further information on the laws governing funerals in your state, how to make funeral arrangements, or the options available, contact Funeral Consumers Alliance, P.O. Box 10, Hinesburg, VT 05461; (802) 482-3437; www.funerals.org. This is a consumer organization whose purpose is to provide information that will help people to plan a "meaningful, dignified, and affordable" funeral. If you are one of those people who feel that too much money is spent on funerals and you would prefer something simple such as a "plain pine box," you will find their information describing your options with respect to services, caskets, embalming, cremation, etc. most helpful.

The Cremation Association of North America, 401 North Michigan Avenue, Chicago IL 60611, (312) 644-6610, www.cremationassociation.org is an association of over 1,200 crematories, cemeteries, and funeral homes that offer cremation.

A free copy of "Funerals: A Consumer Guide" and additional information concerning the Funeral Rule are available on the FTC website at www.ftc.gov. You may also telephone or write the Consumer Response Center, Federal Trade Commission, 600 Pennsylvania, NW, Room H-130, Washington, DC 20580-0001; 1-877-FTC-HELP (1-877-382-4357).

Pre-Paid Funerals

Many funeral directors urge consumers to pay for their own funerals in advance—termed "pre-need"—which they say will not only save grief-stricken survivors the trouble of making funeral arrangements but also will save money by locking-in the current price for funeral goods and services.

In principle this may seem prudent. In practice it requires that consumers take a number of precautions to insure that they actually get the funeral they purchased. Reportedly, in a number of instances, prepaid funeral funds have gone not into a trust account or life insurance policy but into a managed-money account to which the funeral director may have direct access. In several instances, the funeral director has used the funds for other purposes or the managed accounts have gone bankrupt.

145

If you are considering prepaid funeral arrangements, you should determine how your funds will be held in trust. If they are not placed in an escrow account, trust account, or life insurance policy to which the funeral firm does not have access, do not do business with that firm.

Equally important, make sure that you can get a refund if you change your mind. You might move, or you might decide that you want to be buried, after all, instead of cremated. Where funds are held in a deposit fund or trust account at a financial institution, you should be able to receive a refund in accordance with the terms of the written contract (there probably will be a penalty for early withdrawal). If the funds are poured into a life insurance or annuity contract, the terms of the prepaid arrangement should permit you to receive the cash surrender value of the contract.

Burial Insurance

There is an alternative to "prepaid" funeral arrangements that can achieve many of the same goals – namely, to save your survivors the expense of your funeral – but provide some flexibility that is not available when you contract far ahead of time with a particular funeral provider. Very simply, you can "pre-fund" your own funeral, to be carried out according to your instructions, by purchasing a life insurance policy with a death benefit adequate to cover the costs of the funeral you desire. Although it does not relieve your survivors of all funeral tasks, such a plan will insure that the funds are available when needed—and could cost substantially less than the prepaid funeral, depending on the premiums that you must pay to keep the insurance in force before you die. For example, if you purchase a level-premium policy and die shortly after the policy becomes effective, your estate probably will save much of the cost of your funeral. Of course, you have to qualify for life insurance. If you are in poor health, you may not be able to get insurance or the death benefit may not justify the premium costs.

Low-Cost or No-Cost Alternatives

For those who do not want a "conventional" funeral, there are legal non-funeral options that may be appealing. There are four legal methods of disposition of human remains: burial, entombment, cremation, or donation for scientific study.

146

Many large medical centers accept donations of human remains for purposes of teaching or research. In most instances the facility will pay a donation fee upon receipt of the remains. In many states, such donations are regulated by a state Anatomical Board that pays the fees to the donor's estate, which then can either be retained as part of the estate or donated to a charity of one's choosing. Arrangements should be made in advance. For information about the forms you must complete and the procedures that must be followed, contact the medical facility to which you wish to donate your remains. All such donations are revocable by alternate instructions prior to death.

We also are aware of at least one cremation service that, at a significantly lower cost than conventional funerals and burials, will transport the remains from the place of death to a holding facility pending procurement of the signed death certificate and disposition permit; cremate and scatter the remains at sea or in a rose garden, or return them to the family, as desired; and supply urn and professional and administrative services as needed. For further information, contact The Neptune Society, 4312 Woodman Avenue, Third Floor, Sherman Oaks, California 91423; (888) 637-8863; www.neptunesociety.com. This is a for-profit firm that is licensed in ten states (AZ, CA, CO, FL, IL, IA, MO, NY, OR, WA).

Finally, in some states, such as Texas, a family may bury its own dead without using a licensed funeral director. Do-it-yourself burials require at minimum a statement of death, death certificate, and burial-transit permit. In many states, local ordinances govern do-it-yourself burials, which may be prohibited in some jurisdictions. To obtain information about laws governing funerals by non-licensed family members, contact the Funeral Consumers Alliance, cited above.

APPENDIX A
A PARTING THOUGHT ON PUBLIC HEALTH CARE

POPULAR sentiment in favor of some type of socialized health insurance evidently flourishes in the United States today. For example, to the extent that there is dissatisfaction among the elderly with the new Medicare prescription drug plan enacted in 2003, it is chiefly because it is said to afford "too few benefits." Given the political clout of the elderly, it seems very unlikely that nominal Medicare benefits will be *reduced* anytime soon (though *actual* benefits may continue to be curtailed through reduced reimbursements from Medicare to health care providers.)

At the same time, there appears to be growing public recognition that the present arrangement places an unfair burden on others. For example, families with young children, who are thought to be just as deserving of access to health care as are either the elderly or Medicaid recipients who pay nothing for their care, are disadvantaged under the present system. Today, many are forced to contribute precious financial resources for the care of others while they themselves must go without. Some states are trying to get relatively well-off Medicaid beneficiaries to pay more of their share: already three states have applied to the federal government to toughen their Medicaid rules to lengthen the "look back period" for gift transfers that could result in the denial of a Medicaid application, from the current three years to as long as six years.

An evidently growing segment of the public believes that an equitable solution to this disparate treatment is a publicly financed universal health care system that would favor no class of beneficiaries over any other and, it is thought, would be less costly than either the current "patchwork" health care arrangements or a purely market-based regime. As appealing as it may seem at first blush, from the perspective of both sound economics and social ethics, there would appear to be many difficulties with this approach.

Health Care Spending in Perspective

One of the principal advantages a publicly financed health care system is said to have over a market-based system is that a public system would be better equipped to "contain costs." As a primary example of the deficiencies of market-based medicine, advocates of universal health insurance cite that, as a percent of Gross Domestic Product (GDP), health care expenditures in the United States are greater than in any other major industrialized nation—and still are increasing.

Although the numbers may be accurate, the argument is spurious. A relatively high level of spending *per se* in no way reflects "deficiencies" in the way health care is provided. From a market perspective there is no rationale for believing that *any* particular level of health care expenditures represents the optimum. Individuals decide how much they wish to spend on their health in relation to other things, and very often that decision depends on the proportion of their wealth that *must* be spent on life's other necessities—food, shelter, clothing, etc. It is a matter of supposition that in economies where the necessities of life require less of one's resources, a relatively greater proportion will be directed toward improving health and longevity. That the United States spends proportionally more on health care than any other country may indicate not that we somehow have "fallen behind" in managing health care, but that we have advanced economically beyond other nations—to the point that health concerns are markedly greater priorities here than elsewhere.

Hence, that we choose to devote more of our resources toward improving our health might reflect our relatively greater affluence. And there is ample reason to suppose that an even greater portion of our resources may be channeled that way in the future, especially if medical advances continue to encourage even greater consumption. Who would not want to invest in the discovery of a fountain of youth, which is what modern medicine in effect promises today? It should come as no surprise that the "product" of medicine in the United States, which has enabled millions to enjoy longer lives in better health than ever before, in recent decades has attained greater appeal in relation to other things.

Or to put it another way, in the last three decades consumer spending on, say, recreational goods and services has increased markedly as a proportion of total spending. Yet no one complains that the relative level of spending on such items as stereos, VCRs, speedboats, or Las Vegas vacations, which is much higher in the United States than in most other countries, is "too high." Why, then, the preoccupation with containing the level of spending on health care, especially when it would seem to mirror priorities that, literally, are healthy ones?

Beyond this, our relatively greater health expenditures also reflect the aging of America and the fact that for the majority of the population life expectancies have increased markedly. In relation to GDP, health care expenditures can be expected to increase disproportionately as the proportion of the elderly and longevity increase. The reason is uncomplicated: the aged contribute proportionally less to the other GDP components than they do to its health care component. (The elderly consume relatively more health services than other age groups at the same time that, as retirees, they contribute less to the non-consumption components of GDP.) In part, then, our current level of spending on health care has been a predictable result of demographic contours that have little if anything to do with the way the health care markets operate.

Subsidies Create Price Spirals

But perhaps the greatest misunderstanding of health care cost pressures involves the Medicare and Medicaid subsidies. Appeals for greater government intervention in our health care system often lay the blame for "high costs" on mismanaged hospitals, greedy doctors and lawyers (who prosecute malpractice suits), and profit-seeking insurance companies. But the chief culprits are Medicare and Medicaid themselves.

It is an axiom of economics that *subsidies of any kind create shortages that promote price spirals*. Subsidies affect supply, demand, and prices. Agricultural subsidies often involve restrictions on supply as well as "price supports" in the form of government purchases at above-market prices.

In the instances of Medicare and Medicaid, which enlarge demand for medical services, the fully predictable result has been to increase the prices. It would seem that whenever a third party assumes responsibility for payments there is a subsidy effect, with demand tending to increase and prices tending to be pressured upward. For example, it almost surely is not coincidental that with the advent of tax-exempt employer sponsored group health insurance after World War II, health care prices began to increase faster than the prices of other things. Indeed, the prices of health-care-related goods and services as measured by the Consumer Price Index (CPI) have increased faster than the prices of other goods and services in all but six years since 1947. Medicare hugely increased health care subsidies to elderly consumers, and the prices of Medicare-covered services skyrocketed after the program was introduced in 1966.

Subsidies Foster Scarcities—and Rationing

Even less well understood by many is the tendency for health care subsidies over the long run to create scarcities. Producer subsidies to farmers or manufacturers are designed to foster scarcity directly by keeping goods from reaching the market (*e.g.*, payments to farmers to keep land idle, grain purchase and storage programs, or quotas on auto imports). But consumer subsidies indirectly produce the same effects, which, in the case of health care, are especially injurious.

Stated simply, consumer subsidies for health care trigger a spiral of events that begins with accelerated demand and culminates in rationing, in which access to goods and services can be manipulated to suit the wishes of those with the greatest political clout. This has happened in virtually every country that has adopted state-sponsored universal health insurance.

Ultimately, access to care is decided politically by the elite in power (one shudders to think what preferences some political factions might legislate). The eventual result is that someone other than the patient and the physician—usually a bureaucrat administering the "regulations" who has no interest in the outcome—decides who does or does not get what kind of care. A chief problem with the politically based allocation of scarce resources is that almost inevitably those resources are used in ways favored by the elite in control, but which may not be (indeed, almost never are) their most efficient use. Medical entitlements to sophisticated procedures such as heart bypass operations may be enormously politically attractive, but they are not cost effective in comparison with, say, immunization programs.

The point is that, wherever resources are scarce, all needs cannot be satisfied, and someone must decide how they will be distributed. In a market-based health care system, those decisions are made by the patient and doctor, who together arrive at the most cost-effective course of treatment within the range of affordability. Under this arrangement, virtually everyone who needs it gets some care. In a socialized health care environment, someone other than the patient or the doctor makes those decisions based on priorities that often are mechanistic and that may deny all care to those who do not meet certain qualifications (say, because you are "too old" or have "no dependents" or are not in a "crucial occupation").

The flip side of this situation is "supply side" scarcity that results from restraints that often are concurrently imposed on the providers of the subsidized goods and services. In the case of Medicare and Medicaid, for example, at least one "cost containment" initiative undertaken in the 1980s appears to have had measurable effects on the supply of one health care commodity. The supply of community hospital beds has dropped sharply since Medicare's substitution of the DRG prospective payment system for reimbursement of actual charges. (The average length of stay for Medicare patients decreased markedly following the introduction of the DRG system. Under that system, hospitals are paid a fixed fee for a given diagnosis and they benefit financially if actual costs are less than the payment they receive—that is, if patients are discharged quickly.)

Beyond this, regulation of physicians' charges under Medicare's "relative value scale" reimbursement policy almost surely will have unintended consequences over the long run. The reasoning behind the "relative value" policy is roughly as follows: on the basis of the time and resources it takes them to learn their respective specialties and the time they actually spend with patients, some doctors are paid "too much" and some "too little" under market-based pricing, and therefore all doctors' charges should be regulated to reflect more accurately the relative value of their inputs.

Such logic is seriously flawed and betrays a lack of understanding of how prices (doctors' fees) promote self-regulating markets. It appears to depend on the assumption that the current allocation of human resources in the training of physicians reflects "optimal utility." In fact, the very presence of the "imbalances" that the relative value regime seeks to redress is *prima facie* evidence that this cannot be so. The genius of the market is that when some jobs are paid "too much" while others are paid "too little," soon there will be more people available to do the higher paying job. Markets rarely, if ever, reach, let alone sustain, equilibrium. But the continual process of adjustment insures that, all else equal, vast imbalances cannot persist.

To enshrine existing imbalances by way of an income-based policy, which is what the "relative value scale" reimbursement scheme does, is economic insanity. Over the long run, it can be expected to drive talented individuals *away* from those medical occupations that, as evidenced by market prices, are most valued. Indeed, the long-run effects of price restraints, rationing of health care and the concomitant dilution of physician authority, and the many other attributes of politically regulated medicine are not hard to predict: they very likely will drive talented individuals away from medicine. In their most completely developed expression (*i.e.*, in fully socialized medical environments) such restraints have been a powerful prescription for scarcities, even of the most elementary medical goods and services. Reportedly, it was hard to find even a bottle of aspirin in Soviet Russia during its final years.

In a more recent example, Canada, which has essentially eliminated free markets in medical care, has seen its health services become nearly as scarce as Ontario orange groves. Of the industrialized countries that have universal access, publicly-funded health care systems, Canada uniquely bans private medicine, including private insurance and private hospitals that compete for patient demand. And, unlike most other universal access countries, Canada also does not charge user fees, which force health-care consumers to participate in the costs of the care they demand. The Fraser Institute (a Vancouver-based think tank) reports that Canada ranks 17th out of 20 industrialized, universal-access countries in doctors per thousand people. Yet in 1970, the year when public insurance first fully applied to physician services, Canada ranked fourth in that category. Among these same countries, Canadians are most likely to wait more than a month for non-emergency surgery and had the greatest difficulty accessing a specialist. Though Canada is the number one health-care spender among these countries, it ranks 18th out of 23 in access to MRIs and 17th out of 22 in access to CT scanners. The median wait for an MRI from the time of referral was seven months in 2001.

Problems with Health Care "Rights"

Many people apparently believe that equal access to health care is a "right" which everyone in an advanced country such as the United

States ought to enjoy. At the very least, however, the notion of rights of any kind requires that they be describable. In the case of health care, this would seem to imply some related level of benefits that is obvious. But it isn't. Some people rush to the doctor for every stubbed toe while others may be on their death beds before they will consent to see a doctor; the hypochondriac demands more care than the Christian Scientist.

As a result, any health care "rights" assigned to individuals with such disparate behavior will, in all likelihood, be viewed differently by their possessors. Some will view their rights far more expansively than others. If health care rights are viewed broadly to include treatment on demand, it is the hypochondriac who will consume scarce resources at the expense of others. If such rights are not so viewed, as they almost certainly would not be, then the problem of rationing is reintroduced, and the "rights" made conditional—which is but another way of saying there are no rights at all.

The larger problem is that human health and human behavior often are directly linked. Of course, many people who are "health conscious" and act in ways to promote their own good health still have heart attacks, get cancer, or suffer illness no matter how assiduously they follow a health regimen. But others by free choice engage in behavior that is known to lead directly to illness or accident. Should others be forced to pay the costs of care of those who persist in behavior that is risky? In this context, health care rights that convey equal access to care, or care on demand, would seem to imply disregard for the possible individual and social advantages of one type of behavior over another. Put another way, they would seem to subsidize pathological behavior which, broadly described, accounts for a substantial portion of health care expenditures in the United States today.

APPENDIX B

For free copies of these Medicare publications, call 1-800-Medicare

Pub Number	Name	Information
02240	Publication Catalog	This booklete contains information on free booklets about Medicare and related topics (9 pages).
10050	Medicare & You 2004	Summary of Medicare benefits, rights and obligations (88 pages).
10108	Medicare.gov Brochure	Overview of Medicare internet site. (2 pages).
02154	Medicare Hospice Benefits	An explanation of Medicare hospice care coverage (14 pages).
10116	Your Medicare Benefits	An explanation of Part A and Part B (56 pages).
10153	Medicare Coverage of Skilled Nursing Facility Care	Explanation of Medicare covered skilled care, your rights and protections (48 pages).
10184	Medicare and Your Mental health Benefits	Explanation of mental health benefits, who is eligible, and how payment is made (12 pages).
10969	Medicare and Home Health Care	Explanation of Medicare home health care coverage (32 pages).
11021	Medicare Coverage of Ambulance Services	Explanation of Part B coverage of ambulance services (15 pages).
11022	Medicare Coverage of Diabetes Supplies and Services	Explanation regarding the diabetes supplies and services that Medicare helps pay for (30 pages).
11037	Medicare Coverage Outside of the United States	Information about Medicare coverage of health services when beneficiaries travel outside the United States (4 pages).

APPENDIX B (CONTINUED)

Publication Number	Name	Information
10134	Does Your Doctor or Supplier Accept Assignment?	Explanation about how assignment can save you money (20 pages).
02110	2003 Guide To Health Insurance For People With Medicare	Contains information on choosing a Medigap policy to supplement original Medicare (92 pages).
02219	Choosing a Medicare Health Plan: A Guide for People with Medicare	Explanation of Medicare health plans and how to compare them to make the choice that is best for you (44 pages).
10144	Your Guide To Private Fee-For-Service Plans	Information about Medicare private fee-for-service plans (24 pages).
02174	Guide to Choosing a Nursing Home	Information about how to choose a nursing home (64 pages).
02223	Choosing Long-Term Care	A guide to help Medicare beneficiaries choose a long-term care facility (44 pages).
10180	Choosing a Doctor	A guide to help Medicare beneficiaries choose a doctor (36 pages).
10181	Choosing a Hospital	A guide to help Medicare beneficiaries choose a hospital (24 pages).
10119	Medicare Appeals and Grievances	How to file an appeal or grievance (1 page).
10110	Medicare Preventive Services To Keep You Healthy	Description of preventive services covered by Medicare (6 pages).

PUBLICATIONS
AND SUSTAINING MEMBERSHIPS

You can receive our twice monthly *Research Reports* and monthly *Economic Education Bulletin* by entering a **Sustaining Membership** for only $16 quarterly or $59 annually. If you wish to receive only the *Economic Education Bulletin*, you may enter an **Education Membership** for $25 annually.

INVESTMENT GUIDE

At your request, AIER will forward your payment for a subscription to the *INVESTMENT GUIDE* published by American Investment Services, Inc. (AIS). The *GUIDE* is issued once a month at a price of $59 per year (add $8 for foreign airmail). It provides guidance to investors, both working and retired, of modest and large means, to help them preserve the real value of their wealth during these difficult financial times. AIS is wholly owned by AIER and is the only investment advisory endorsed by AIER.

CONTACT US ONLINE

www.aier.org
aierpubs@aier.org